McDougal Littell
MATH
Course 3

Larson   Boswell   Kanold   Stiff

Assessment Book

The formal assessment of the Assessment Book includes a diagnostic pre-course test, a post-course test, quizzes, chapter tests, standardized tests, unit tests, and cumulative tests organized by chapter and unit. The alternative assessment includes various forms of alternative assessment for each chapter. The Assessment Book also includes recording sheets to track individual student progress or class progress on the diagnostic pre-course test and the post-course test.

McDougal Littell
A DIVISION OF HOUGHTON MIFFLIN COMPANY

Evanston, Illinois • Boston • Dallas

Contributing Authors

The authors wish to thank the following individuals for their contributions to the Assessment Book.

Joanne Ricci
Dr. Marc A. Sylvester

ISBN 13: 978-0-618-74101-4
ISBN 10: 0-618-74101-1

23456789–VOM–10 09 08 07

Contents

COURSE 3 Assessment Book

Contents

Contents

Contents

Descriptions of Resources

This Assessment Book is organized by chapters and units. The following materials are provided:

Diagnostic Pre-Course Test   This test covers material from previous courses that students should have some familiarity with. The Skills Review Handbook in the Student Edition is an excellent source for students needing remediation on certain topics.

Quizzes   There are two quizzes per chapter corresponding to the Review Quizzes in the Student Edition. These quizzes can be used to assess student progress on three or four lessons.

Chapter Tests A, B, and C   These are tests that cover the most important skills taught in the chapter. There are three levels of tests: A (basic), B (average), and C (advanced).

Standardized Test   This test also covers the most important skills taught in the chapter, but questions are in multiple-choice, short response, and extended response format. (See *Alternative Assessment* for multi-step problems.)

Alternative Assessment and Math Journal   A journal exercise has students write about the mathematics in the chapter. A multi-step problem has students apply a variety of skills from the chapter and explain their reasoning. Solutions and a four-point rubric are included.

Unit Tests   These are tests that cover the most important skills taught in each unit. There is one test for each unit.

Cumulative Tests   These are tests that cover the most important skills taught in the current unit and all preceding units. There is one cumulative test at the end of each unit.

Post-Course Test   This test covers the most important skills taught throughout the entire course. It can be used as a full-year final exam or as a indicator of how well students are prepared for their next course in mathematics.

Algebra Readiness Test   This test covers the most important algebra skills taught throughout the entire course. It can be used as an indicator of how well students are prepared for an Algebra 1 course.

Diagnostic Pre-Course Test and Post-Course Test Performance Records   The Diagnostic Pre-Course recording sheet is organized by Skills Review Handbook topic and the Post-Course recording sheet is organized by lesson title. They help you monitor the performance of individual students on the topics covered in the Skills Review Handbook and the textbook.

Diagnostic Pre-Course Test and Post-Course Test Item Analyses   These recording sheets are organized by test item. They help you monitor the performance of an entire class on each test item. The Skills Review Handbook topic associated with each Diagnostic Pre-Course test item is indicated. The lesson number associated with each Post-Course test item is indicated.

Gridding Sheets   A reproducible sheet with twelve blank grids is provided for use in conjunction with test items and selected exercises so that students can gain experience completing grids in a testing situation. Spaces are provided to write in the appropriate exercise numbers.

Name _____

Date _____

Pre-Course Test

For use before Chapter 1

Write the number in expanded form.

1. 1109 **2.** 1,986,432 **3.** 56.19 **4.** 286.393

Round the number to the place value of the underlined digit.

5. 2<u>3</u>9 **6.** 14<u>8</u>7 **7.** 740,<u>6</u>92 **8.** 63,4<u>6</u>3

9. 16.1<u>3</u>9 **10.** 284.<u>1</u>9 **11.** 758.9<u>2</u>9 **12.** 0.1<u>4</u>28

Test the number for divisibility by 2, 3, 4, 5, 6, 8, 9, and 10.

13. 128 **14.** 432 **15.** 22,480 **16.** 638,928

Write the mixed number as an improper fraction.

17. $2\frac{2}{3}$ **18.** $9\frac{4}{9}$ **19.** $21\frac{14}{15}$ **20.** $17\frac{9}{11}$

Write the improper fraction as a mixed number.

21. $\frac{12}{5}$ **22.** $\frac{19}{2}$ **23.** $\frac{143}{9}$ **24.** $\frac{162}{13}$

The table shows the number of students in Mrs. Stewart's class that own each type of pet. Use the table to write the specified ratio.

	Dogs	Cats	Snakes
Girls	6	9	1
Boys	13	4	3

25. Number of girls who own dogs to number of boys who own dogs

26. Number of girls who own cats to number of girls who own dogs or cats

27. Number of boys who own dogs to number of boys who own dogs or cats

28. Number of boys and girls who own snakes to number of boys and girls who own a dog, cat, or snake

Answers

1. _____
2. _____
3. _____
4. _____
5. _____
6. _____
7. _____
8. _____
9. _____
10. _____
11. _____
12. _____
13. _____
14. _____
15. _____
16. _____
17. _____
18. _____
19. _____
20. _____
21. _____
22. _____
23. _____
24. _____
25. _____
26. _____
27. _____
28. _____

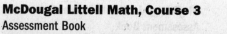

McDougal Littell Math, Course 3
Assessment Book

1

COURSE 3 Continued

Pre-Course Test

For use before Chapter 1

Find the sum or difference.

29. $9.27 + 3.64$

30. $2.938 + 3.215$

31. $10.29 - 5.57$

32. $56.123 - 37.975$

33. $\dfrac{5}{7} + \dfrac{6}{7}$

34. $\dfrac{8}{13} + \dfrac{3}{13}$

35. $\dfrac{10}{17} - \dfrac{2}{17}$

36. $\dfrac{19}{21} - \dfrac{12}{21}$

37. Your class is selling tickets for the school play. Your class sold 57 tickets on Wednesday, 65 tickets on Thursday, and 113 tickets on Friday. How many tickets were sold on these three days?

38. You buy a DVD for $17.38. You pay with a $20 bill. How much change should you receive?

Find the product. Then simplify, if possible.

39. $10 \times \dfrac{1}{2}$

40. $3 \times \dfrac{4}{3}$

41. $\dfrac{11}{13} \times \dfrac{5}{11}$

42. $\dfrac{2}{9} \times \dfrac{6}{13}$

Find the product.

43. $\begin{array}{r} 1.6 \\ \times\ 13 \\ \hline \end{array}$

44. $\begin{array}{r} 532 \\ \times\ 6.05 \\ \hline \end{array}$

45. $\begin{array}{r} 2.913 \\ \times\ 53 \\ \hline \end{array}$

46. $\begin{array}{r} 39.046 \\ \times\ 121 \\ \hline \end{array}$

Find the quotient.

47. $10.2 \div 3$

48. $31 \div 6.2$

49. $78 \div 2.13$

50. $86.91 \div 15$

51. A cookie recipe calls for $3\dfrac{1}{2}$ cups of flour. You have $10\dfrac{1}{2}$ cups of flour. How many batches of cookies can you make?

52. You mailed 19 postcards and the stamps cost $.23 each. How much did you pay for postage?

53. You bought 7 packs of trading cards for $37.03. How much did you pay for each pack of trading cards?

Answers

29. _____

30. _____

31. _____

32. _____

33. _____

34. _____

35. _____

36. _____

37. _____

38. _____

39. _____

40. _____

41. _____

42. _____

43. _____

44. _____

45. _____

46. _____

47. _____

48. _____

49. _____

50. _____

51. _____

52. _____

53. _____

2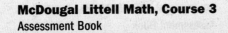
McDougal Littell Math, Course 3
Assessment Book

Name _____ Date _____

Pre-Course Test
For use before Chapter 1

In Exercises 54–57, use the diagram.

54. Name four points.

55. Name three rays.

56. Name two lines.

57. Name three line segments.

Name the angle in three ways.

58.

59.

60.

Use a ruler to measure the line segment in inches.

61. _____

62. _____

Use a ruler to measure the line segment in centimeters.

63. _____

64. _____

Use a ruler to draw a segment with the given length.

65. $1\frac{3}{4}$ inches

66. $2\frac{3}{16}$ inches

67. $\frac{15}{16}$ inch

68. 1.7 centimeters

69. 3.8 centimeters

70. 5.1 centimeters

Answers

54. _____
55. _____
56. _____
57. _____
58. _____
_____
_____
_____
59. _____
_____
_____
60. _____
_____
61. _____
62. _____
63. _____
64. _____
65. See left.
66. See left.
67. See left.
68. See left.
69. See left.
70. See left.

Name _____ Date _____

Pre-Course Test

For use before Chapter 1

In Exercises 71–73, use a protractor to measure the angle.

71.

72.

73.

74. Use a protractor to draw angles measuring 27°, 94°, and 163°.

75. Use a compass to draw a circle with a radius of $\frac{1}{2}$ inch.

76. Use a compass to draw a circle with a diameter of 5 centimeters.

Answers

71. _____

72. _____

73. _____

74. ____See left.____

75. ____See left.____

76. ____See left.____

77. ____See left.____

78. ____See left.____

79. _____

_____

80. _____

_____

81. _____

82. _____

In Exercises 77 and 78, use the three segments.

A ——————————— B C ———— D E ——————————————— F

77. Use a straightedge and a compass to draw a segment whose length is the sum of the lengths of the three given segments.

78. Use a straightedge and a compass to draw a segment whose length is the difference of $\overline{EF}$ and $\overline{CD}$.

In Exercises 79–82, use the line plot that shows the number of hours the students in your class study each week.

79. What was the most frequent response? What does this mean?

80. What was the least frequent response? What does this mean?

81. How many students study 9 hours or more each week?

82. How many more students study 10 hours each week than 8 hours each week?

4 **McDougal Littell Math, Course 3**
Assessment Book

Name _____ Date _____

Pre-Course Test
For use before Chapter 1

Make a line plot of the data.

83. In a survey, 23 people were asked how many books they read over a three month period. Their responses were: 5, 1, 0, 8, 4, 5, 1, 2, 2, 0, 4, 12, 9, 0, 3, 2, 1, 6, 2, 2, 0, 3, and 7.

In Exercises 84–86, use the bar graph that shows the survey results for students' favorite types of books to read.

84. How many students chose science fiction as their favorite type of book?

85. What is the most popular type of book? What is the least popular type of book?

86. Estimate the total number of students who chose sports books and history books.

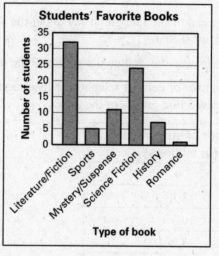

87. The table shows the number of electronic items for 30 households. Draw a bar graph for the data.

Item	Number of Households
Cellular phone	17
Digital camera	3
DVD player	13
Home computer	24
Satellite television	6

Answers

83. _____ See left. _____

84. _____

85. _____

_____

86. _____

_____

87. _____ See left. _____

Name _____ Date _____

Pre-Course Test

For use before Chapter 1

In Exercises 88 and 89, use the line graph that shows the number of sheep and lambs on farms in the United States.

Answers

88. _____

_____

_____

89. _____

_____

90. _____See left._____

91. _____See left._____

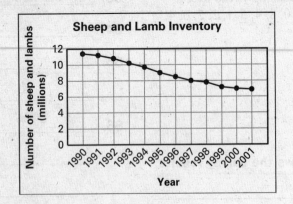

88. What does the overall trend of the line graph say about the sheep and lamb inventory in the United States?

89. Between which two years was the change the greatest? the least?

90. The table shows the number of cellular telephone subscribers from 1992 through 2002. Draw a line graph for the data.

Year	Number of subscribers (in millions)
1992	8.9
1993	13.1
1994	19.3
1995	28.2
1996	38.2
1997	48.7
1998	60.8
1999	76.3
2000	97.0
2001	118.4
2002	134.6

91. Of the whole numbers from 30 through 50, set *A* consists of the numbers that are divisible by 2 and set *B* consists of the numbers that are divisible by 3. Draw a Venn Diagram of the sets described.

McDougal Littell Math, Course 3
Assessment Book

Name _____ Date _____

Quiz 1

For use with Lessons 1.1–1.4

Use the graph at the right that shows the number of students involved in certain after-school activities.

1. Which activity has the most students?

2. About how many students are in the drama club?

3. Would a histogram be an appropriate display for the data?

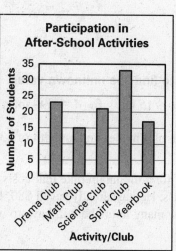

Participation in After-School Activities

Evaluate the expression.

4. $17 + 8 \cdot 3$

5. $32 \div 4 + 7 \cdot 2$

6. $\dfrac{72}{13 - 4}$

7. $21 \div [(7 + 2) \div 3]$

8. $2^3 + (5 + 3)^2$

9. $5^2 + 2 \cdot 17$

Evaluate the expression for the given value of the variable.

10. $7a - 4 - 11$ when $a = 4$

11. $3 \cdot 7 + b \cdot 9$ when $b = 5$

12. $(c + 8)^2 - 4 \cdot 5$ when $c = 3$

13. $12 \cdot 6 \div (8 - x)^3$ when $x = 6$

Answers

1. _____
2. _____
3. _____
4. _____
5. _____
6. _____
7. _____
8. _____
9. _____
10. _____
11. _____
12. _____
13. _____

Name _____ Date _____

Quiz 2
For use with Lessons 1.5–1.7

Solve the equation using mental math.

Answers

1. $k - 18 = 13$

2. $m + 27 = 42$

1. _____

3. $12n = 72$

4. $\dfrac{56}{q} = 8$

2. _____

3. _____

Use the distance formula to find the unknown value.

4. _____

5. $d = $ _____, $r = 8$ mi/h, $t = 15$ h

6. $d = 390$ m, $r = 60$ mi/h, $t = $ _____

5. _____

7. A rectangle has a length of 9 inches and a width of 13 inches. Find the perimeter and area.

6. _____

8. Logan is saving money for a mountain bike that costs $195. He earns $10 an hour cutting grass. He has already saved $80. Use a problem solving plan to find how many hours he will have to work to earn the rest of the money.

7. _____

8. _____

Name _____ Date _____

Chapter Test A

For use after Chapter 1

Use the graph at the right that shows the number of musicians playing each instrument in an orchestra.

1. What type of graph is shown?

2. Which instrument has the most musicians?

3. Which instruments have the same number of musicians?

4. Which instrument has the fewest musicians?

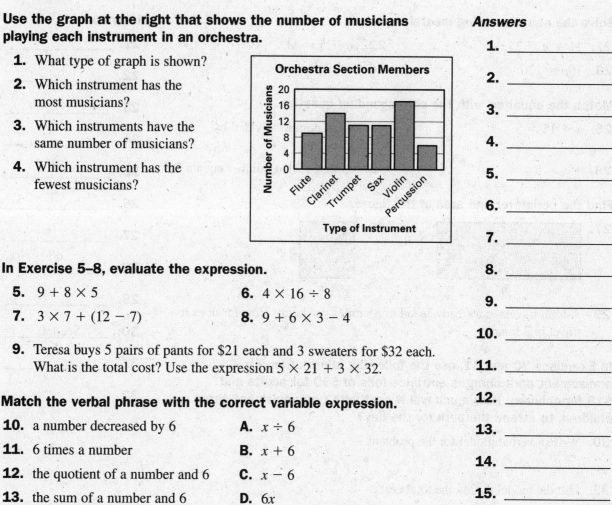

Orchestra Section Members

In Exercise 5–8, evaluate the expression.

5. $9 + 8 \times 5$

6. $4 \times 16 \div 8$

7. $3 \times 7 + (12 - 7)$

8. $9 + 6 \times 3 - 4$

9. Teresa buys 5 pairs of pants for $21 each and 3 sweaters for $32 each. What is the total cost? Use the expression $5 \times 21 + 3 \times 32$.

Match the verbal phrase with the correct variable expression.

10. a number decreased by 6   A. $x \div 6$

11. 6 times a number   B. $x + 6$

12. the quotient of a number and 6 C. $x - 6$

13. the sum of a number and 6   D. $6x$

Evaluate the expression for the given value of the variable.

14. $9x + 7$ when $x = 3$

15. $\dfrac{10a + 8}{a}$ when $a = 4$

Evaluate the power.

16. 6^2 17. 4^3 18. 3^4

Evaluate the expression.

19. $(4 \times 2)^2 - 12$

20. $27 \div (8 - 5)^2$

Answers

1. _____
2. _____
3. _____
4. _____
5. _____
6. _____
7. _____
8. _____
9. _____
10. _____
11. _____
12. _____
13. _____
14. _____
15. _____
16. _____
17. _____
18. _____
19. _____
20. _____

Name _____ Date _____

Chapter Test A

For use after Chapter 1

Solve the equation using mental math.

21. $11 + n = 24$　　　　　　**22.** $m - 5 = 17$

23. $10p = 120$　　　　　　**24.** $r \div 7 = 9$

Match the equation with the corresponding question.

25. $x \div 15 = 5$

A. What number divided by 15 equals 5?

26. $15x = 5$

B. 15 times what number equals 5?

Find the perimeter and area of the figure.

27.

3 in.

8 in.

28.

9 m

9 m

29. A train travels at a steady speed of 85 miles per hour. How far does it travel in 3 hours?

In Exercises 30 and 31, use the following information. An amusement park charges entrance fees of \$30 for adults and \$18 for children. How much will it cost with two adults and three children, to attend the park for the day?

30. Write a verbal model for the problem.

31. Use the model to find the total cost.

32. You spend 2 hours on the computer each night during the week and 3 hours each night during the weekend. Use a problem solving plan to find how many hours you spend each week on the computer.

Answers

21. _____

22. _____

23. _____

24. _____

25. _____

26. _____

27. _____

28. _____

29. _____

30. _____ See left.

31. _____

32. _____

Name _____ Date _____

Chapter Test B

For use after Chapter 1

In Exercises 1 and 2, use the table that shows the number of students buying lunch in the cafeteria.

Days	Monday	Tuesday	Wednesday	Thursday	Friday
Students	62	65	75	68	88

1. Would a bar graph or histogram be better to display this data? Why?

2. How many bars would you use for a bar graph of this data?

Use the following data: 2, 2, 3, 3, 4, 5, 6, 7

3. Name 3 equal intervals you could use to group this data.

4. What would be the frequency of data in the first interval?

In Exercises 5–10, evaluate the expression.

5. $6 - 8 \times 3 \div 6$

6. $36 + (7 + 5) \div 4$

7. $\dfrac{72}{17 - 5}$

8. $160 \div [8 \times (3 + 2)]$

9. $(3 + 2)^3 \cdot 3 - 8$

10. $140 - (13 - 3)^2 + 3 \times 2^3$

11. A pizza shop charges $7.75 for a large pizza, plus $1.25 for each additional topping. You order a large pizza with three extra toppings. How much will the pizza cost? Use the expression $7.75 + 3(1.25)$.

In Exercises 12–15, evaluate the expression when $x = 10$ and $y = 8$.

12. $120 - x \cdot 6$

13. $3 \cdot (x - 4) + 2 \cdot y - 12$

14. $\dfrac{1}{2} \cdot x + \dfrac{3}{4} \cdot y$

15. $\dfrac{4 \cdot x + y}{0.5 \cdot y}$

16. Write the verbal phrase "The sum of a number and three-eighths" as a variable expression. Let x represent the variable.

17. A window washer charges $3 for a first floor window and $5 for a second floor window. Write a variable expression to find the cost to wash f first floor windows and s second floor windows in a two-story house.

Complete the statement using <, >, or =.

18. 4^2 ____ 2^4

19. 4^5 ____ 3^6

Answers

1. _____
   _____
2. _____
3. _____
4. _____
5. _____
6. _____
7. _____
8. _____
9. _____
10. _____
11. _____
12. _____
13. _____
14. _____
15. _____
16. _____
17. _____
18. _____
19. _____

Name _____ Date _____

Chapter Test B

For use after Chapter 1

Tell whether the value of the variable is a solution of the equation.

20. $54 - c = 18$; $c = 34$

21. $\dfrac{b}{11} = 9$; $b = 99$

Solve the equation using mental math.

22. $32 - z = 14$

23. $9w = 36$

24. $\dfrac{m}{5} = 10$

Find the perimeter and area of the figure.

25.

13 m

21 m

26.

15 cm

15 cm

27. Find the side length of a square with an area of 81 m^2.

In Exercises 28 and 29, use the distance formula to find the unknown value.

28. $d = 117$ mi, $r = 9$ mi/h, $t = $ ____

29. $d = 975$ ft, $r = $ ____, $t = 15$ min

30. An eagle is diving at a rate of 120 feet per second. If it dives for 1.5 seconds at this rate, how far has it descended?

31. A farmer needs to cut 46 acres of hay. It takes him 2 hours to cut the first 10 acres. Use a problem solving plan to find out how many acres he must cut each hour to finish cutting the remaining hay in 6 hours.

32. A school is raising money to buy a $350 dalmatian puppy for a local fire department. They have raised already $120. They hold a car wash that will make $2.50 for each washed car. How many cars must they wash to raise the rest of the money?

Answers

20. _____

21 _____

22. _____

23 _____

24. _____

25. _____

26. _____

27. _____

28. _____

29. _____

30. _____

31. _____

32. _____

Name _____ Date _____

Chapter Test C

For use after Chapter 1

In Exercises 1–3, use the following data that shows the typical numbers of hours 15 students spend on the telephone in a week.

3.6, 2.7, 3.1, 2.1, 1.2, 4.1, 2.3, 3.8,
4.1, 0.8, 1.6, 0.5, 1.3, 2.6, 1.9

1. Write 5 even intervals the data can be grouped into starting with 0 and ending with 4.9.

2. Complete the frequency table at the right.

3. Would a bar graph or histogram represent the data better? Why?

Hours	Tally	Freq.
0−0.9		

4. How do the bars in a histogram differ from the bars in a bar graph?

Evaluate the expression.

5. $\dfrac{16 + 4}{11 - 3 \times 2}$

6. $2 \times 5.6 + 3 \times 3.5$

7. $(17 - 3)^2 + 6^3$

8. $12^2 \div (9 - 5)^2$

Add parentheses to make the statement true.

9. $7 \times 9 - 8 + 7 = 56$

10. $64 \div 11 - 3 + 4 = 12$

In Exercises 11 and 12, evaluate the expression when $x = 3.3$ and $y = 6$.

11. $3x + 5y$

12. $2xy$

13. A distance runner trains on two courses. One course is 3 miles long, and the other is 5 miles long. In a week, she uses the short course s times and the long course ℓ times. Write a variable expression for the number of miles in a week.

14. Eggs cost $1.48 a dozen and milk costs $2.65 a gallon. You have a coupon to get $.75 off the price of 1 gallon of milk. Write a variable expression for the cost of d dozen eggs and g gallons of milk. How much would 3 dozen eggs and 1 gallon of milk cost?

Evaluate the expression when $a = 4$ and $b = 5$.

15. $a^3 b^2$

16. $(a - 2)^5 - (3b \div 5)^2$

Answers

1. _____
2. ___See left.___
3. _____
   _____
4. _____
   _____
5. _____
6. _____
7. _____
8. _____
9. _____
10. _____
11. _____
12. _____
13. _____
14. _____
15. _____
16. _____

In Exercises 17–19, solve the equation using mental math.

Answers

17. $c - 36 = 22$

18. $17m = 170$

19. $52 \div x = 13$

20. A truck loaded with logs weighs 12,760 pounds. The empty truck weighs 4,823 pounds. Write and solve an equation to find the weight of the logs.

21. Tell which of the values, $x = 7, 8,$ or 9, is a solution of the equation $7x - 5 = 6x + 3$.

22. Find the area of a rectangle with a perimeter of 46 feet and a length of 13 feet.

23. Find the side length of a square that has a perimeter of 14 feet.

24. Find the width of a rectangle that has a length of 18 inches and an area of 72 square inches.

25. A dog is running at a speed of 10 miles per hour. He runs for 20 minutes. How far has he traveled?

26. A truck traveling at a steady speed of 60 miles per hour has gone 210 miles. How long has it been driving?

27. A family is making a five-day 2100-mile trip. The first four days they traveled 1755 miles. Use a problem solving plan to find what speed they must travel to complete their trip in 6 hours on the final day.

28. The product of two numbers is 80. Their difference is 11. Find the two numbers.

29. Riding at a steady pace, Michael completed the first 15 miles of a 25-mile bike trip in 45 minutes. He finished the trip at the same rate. What was his total time for the bike trip?

17. _____

18. _____

19. _____

20. _____

21. _____

22. _____

23. _____

24. _____

25. _____

26. _____

27. _____

28. _____

29. _____

Standardized Test

For use after Chapter 1

Multiple Choice

1. The histogram shows the amount of money 40 people spent on a friend's birthday present. About how many people spent $15 or more?

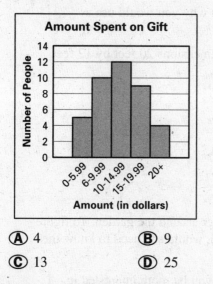

Amount Spent on Gift

Number of People / Amount (in dollars)

$\textbf{A}$ 4 $\textbf{B}$ 9
$\textbf{C}$ 13 $\textbf{D}$ 25

2. Which step should be performed first when finding the sum of 17 and the product of 6 and 8?

$\textbf{F}$ 17 + 6 $\textbf{G}$ 17 + 8
$\textbf{H}$ 6 × 8 $\textbf{I}$ 17 × 6

3. What is the value of the expression $12 + 6 \times (13 - 9)^2 - 2$?

$\textbf{A}$ 36 $\textbf{B}$ 106 $\textbf{C}$ 120 $\textbf{D}$ 586

4. What is the value of $3^5 - 5^3$?

$\textbf{F}$ 0 $\textbf{G}$ 118 $\textbf{H}$ 256 $\textbf{I}$ 368

5. What is the solution of $x \div 15 = 5$?

$\textbf{A}$ 3 $\textbf{B}$ 10 $\textbf{C}$ 20 $\textbf{D}$ 75

6. If $x = 3$ and $y = 6$, which equation is true?

$\textbf{F}$ $2x + 3y = 14$ $\textbf{G}$ $xy = 9$
$\textbf{H}$ $3y = 6x$ $\textbf{I}$ $\frac{y^2}{3x} = 3$

7. Which equation represents this statement: *The product of 12 and a number is 18.*

$\textbf{A}$ $12n = 18$ $\textbf{B}$ $12 + n = 18$
$\textbf{C}$ $12 \div n = 18$ $\textbf{D}$ $\frac{n}{12} = 18$

8. What is the area of a rectangle with a length of 12 inches and a width of 6 inches?

$\textbf{F}$ 18 in.^{2} $\textbf{G}$ 36 in.^{2}
$\textbf{H}$ 54 in.^{2} $\textbf{I}$ 72 in.^{2}

9. A race car is traveling around a track at 180 miles per hour. It keeps this pace for 45 minutes. How many miles has it gone?

$\textbf{A}$ 120 miles $\textbf{B}$ 135 miles
$\textbf{C}$ 160 miles $\textbf{D}$ 210 miles

Short Response

10. You are reading a 306-page book. You have 6 days to read the book before it is due back at the library. Write an equation to find the number of pages you need to read each day p, if you wish to read an equal number of pages each day. Then solve your equation.

Extended Response

11. Two people are taking turns driving a car. The first person drives for 3 hours at 65 miles per hour. The second person drives for 5 hours at 60 miles per hour, but stops for a half-hour rest during that time. Write a verbal model to find the distance traveled. Then use your model to find the distance traveled.

Name _____ Date _____

Alternative Assessment and Math Journal

For use after Chapter 1

Journal   **1. a.** In this chapter, you learned how to use bar graphs and histograms to display data. Describe the difference in appearance of each type of graph. Explain the types of data each graph is better suited to represent and why.

   b. Describe what a verbal model is. Explain why you would use a verbal model.

Multi-Step Problem   **2.** Consider a rectangular flower garden with dimensions 20 feet by 12 feet, as shown below.

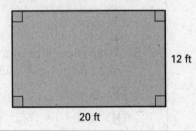

12 ft

20 ft

   a. A landscaper is hired to put a fence border around the garden. To figure out how much fencing material is needed, would she need to know the *area* or the *perimeter* of the garden?

   b. To fertilize the soil in the garden, would you be more interested in finding the *area* or the *perimeter*?

   c. Find the area of the flower garden.

   d. Find the perimeter of the flower garden.

   e. Consider a rectangular vegetable garden that is twice as wide and twice as long as the flower garden shown above. What are the dimensions of the vegetable garden?

   f. Find the perimeter of the vegetable garden. How does this compare to the perimeter of the flower garden?

   g. Find the area of the vegetable garden. How does this compare to the area of the flower garden?

   h. Suppose the length of the vegetable garden were twice the length of the flower garden, but the widths of the two gardens were the same. How do the areas compare?

Name _____ Date _____

Alternative Assessment Rubric

For use after Chapter 1

Journal Solution

1. **a.** Explanations should include these facts: The bars touch at the sides in a histogram, but not in a bar graph; A histogram is used when the data are grouped in evenly-spaced intervals.

   b. Students should describe what a verbal model is and why one is used.

Multi-Step Problem Solution

2. **a.** the perimeter

   b. the area

   c. 240 ft^2

   d. 64 ft

   e. 40 ft by 24 ft

   f. 128 ft; The perimeter of the vegetable garden is twice the perimeter of the flower garden.

   g. 960 ft^2; The area of the vegetable garden is four times the area of the flower garden.

   h. The area of the vegetable garden would be twice the area of the flower garden.

Multi-Step Problem Rubric

4 The student answers all questions correctly and completely, using correct units of measurement.

3 The student answers all of the questions. The student makes an error or two finding values or making comparisons.

2 The student answers all questions, but makes 3 or 4 errors and/or does not use the correct units of measurement.

1 The student has answered fewer than half of the questions correctly. Work may be incomplete and sloppy.

Name _____ Date _____

Quiz 1

For use after Lessons 2.1–2.5

Answers

1. Use a number line to order the integers from least to greatest:
   $-12, 6, 25, -27, 0, -15$.

Write the opposite and the absolute value of the integer.

2. 17

3. -15

4. 0

Evaluate the expression.

5. $-12 + 8$ 6. $-27 + (-12)$

7. $-8 - (-13)$ 8. $-8(14)$

9. $-7(-9)$ 10. $\dfrac{52}{-13}$

In Exercises 11–14, evaluate the expression when $a = -5$, $b = -12$, and $c = 4$.

11. $c - a$ 12. $a - b - c$

13. $ac - bc$ 14. $\dfrac{ab}{c}$

15. Find the mean of the data: $-6, 12, 8, -11, 21, 4, -7$.

16. A hawk flying at a height of 150 feet drops a fish it was carrying in its talons. The equation $h = -16t^2 + 150$ gives the height h, in feet, of the fish after t seconds. Find the height of the fish after 2 seconds and after 3 seconds.

1. _____

2. _____

3. _____

4. _____

5. _____

6. _____

7. _____

8. _____

9. _____

10. _____

11. _____

12. _____

13. _____

14. _____

15. _____

16. _____

_____

McDougal Littell Math, Course 3
Chapter 2   Assessment Book

Name _____ Date _____

Quiz 2

For use after Lessons 2.6–2.8

Evaluate the expression using mental math. Name the property you used.

1. $-52 + 27 + (-35)$

2. $17 + [(-28) + 33]$

3. $5 \cdot (4 \cdot 8)$

4. $50 \cdot (-16) \cdot 2$

Simplify the expression.

5. $7x + 3y - 4x + 2y$

6. $9(x - 1) - 2x + 5$

In Exercises 7–9, use the coordinate plane.

7. Plot and connect the points $A(-6, -9)$, $B(8, -9)$, $C(8, 4)$, and $D(-6, 4)$.

8. Which point lies in Quadrant IV?

9. Find the perimeter of the figure.

10. You are buying 6 boxes of cereal that cost $3.65 each. Use mental math and the distributive property to find the total cost of the cereal.

Answers

1. _____

2. _____

3. _____

4. _____

5. _____

6. _____

7. ____See left.____

8. _____

9. _____

10. _____

Name _____ Date _____

Chapter Test A
For use after Chapter 2

1. Use a number line to order the integers from least to greatest:
0, −27, 15, 8, −13, −32, 11.

Write the opposite and the absolute value of the integer.

2. 19

3. −21

4. −1

Complete the statement with < or >.

5. −6 ____ 4

6. 5 ____ −7

7. −2 ____ 0

8. −12 ____ −15

Use a number line to find the sum.

9. −11 + 8

10. −5 + (−7)

Find the sum or difference.

11. 57 + (−38)

12. −15 + 21 + (−17)

13. 72 − 81

14. −15 − (−12) −8

In Exercises 15 and 16, evaluate the expression when $a = 8$ and $b = −12$.

15. $a - b$

16. $b - a$

17. A store is selling a pair of shoes for $45. During a weekend sale, the shoes are marked down by $18. On Monday, they are marked back up by $9. Two weeks later the shoes are on clearance and marked down by $17. How much will the shoes cost on clearance?

Find the product or quotient.

18. −13(−6)

19. −4(−6)(−8)

20. $\dfrac{-91}{-13}$

21. $\dfrac{0}{-12}$

Answers

1. _____

2. _____

3. _____

4. _____

5. _____

6. _____

7. _____

8. _____

9. _____

10. _____

11. _____

12. _____

13. _____

14. _____

15. _____

16. _____

17. _____

18. _____

19. _____

20. _____

21. _____

Name _____ Date _____

Chapter Test A

For use after Chapter 2

In Exercises 22–24, evaluate the expression when $a = -8$, $b = -12$ and $c = -6$.

22. $ac - b$ **23.** $\dfrac{b}{c}$ **24.** $\dfrac{bc}{a}$

25. The student council has raised $510 for dances. Over the next four weeks they spend $80 each Friday night for dances. How much does the student council have left after the fourth dance?

In Exercises 26–29, match the equation with the property it illustrates.

26. $25x = x \cdot 25$ **A.** Distributive Property

27. $(-8 + 7) + 11 = -8 + (7 + 11)$ **B.** Associative Property of Addition

28. $6(10 + (-1)) = 6(10) + 6(-1)$ **C.** Commutative Property of Multiplication

29. $(3 \cdot 12)15 = 3(12 \cdot 15)$ **D.** Associative Property of Multiplication

Use the distributive property to write an equivalent expression.

30. $9(6 + 8)$ **31.** $-6(5 + 3)$

Simplify the expression by combining like terms.

32. $7x + 12x$ **33.** $15a + 6b - 8a - 9b$

In Exercises 34–37, use the coordinate plane.

34. Give the coordinates of A.

35. Which point has coordinates of $(1, 3)$?

36. Describe the location of point E.

37. Which point is on the y-axis? Give the coordinates of the point.

In Exercises 38–40, use the coordinate plane.

38. Plot $A(3, -4)$

39. Plot $B(-2, -4)$

40. What is the distance from A to B?

Answers

22. _____
23. _____
24. _____
25. _____
26. _____
27. _____
28. _____
29. _____
30. _____
31. _____
32. _____
33. _____
34. _____
35. _____
36. _____
37. _____
38. _____See left._____
39. _____See left._____
40. _____

CHAPTER 2

Chapter Test B
For use after Chapter 2

In Exercises 1–4, complete the statement with < or >.

Answers

1. 13 ____ -15

2. -8 ____ -6

3. -39 ____ 51

4. $|-6|$ ____ 5

5. Use a number line to order the integers from least to greatest:
   $31, -27, 17, 40, -16, -30.$

Simplify the expression.

6. $|-7|$

7. $-(-15)$

8. $-|-8|$

9. $-(-(-1))$

Find the sum or difference.

10. $-102 + (-79)$

11. $-52 - (-36)$

12. $17 + (-28) + (-43)$

13. $-57 - 65 + (-21)$

14. $91 - 43 + (-17)$

15. $-37 - (-63) - 82$

Evaluate the expression when $x = -10$, $y = 7$ and $z = -15$.

16. $x - y - z$

17. $z - (-x) + (-y)$

Complete the statement using *always*, *sometimes*, or *never*.

18. The sum of a positive integer and a negative integer is _____ positive.

19. A negative number minus a negative number is _____ negative.

20. A positive number minus a negative integer is _____ positive.

21. The opposite of the absolute value of a negative integer is _____ positive.

Find the product or quotient.

22. $-13(-24)$

23. $-6(-11)(-3)$

24. $\dfrac{48}{-6}$

25. $\dfrac{-18}{-3}$

Answers

1. _____
2. _____
3. _____
4. _____
5. _____
6. _____
7. _____
8. _____
9. _____
10. _____
11. _____
12. _____
13. _____
14. _____
15. _____
16. _____
17. _____
18. _____
19. _____
20. _____
21. _____
22. _____
23. _____
24. _____
25. _____

Evaluate the expression when $m = -6$, $n = -12$, and $p = 20$.

Answers

26. $-2mnp$

27. $mn - np$

26. _____

28. $\dfrac{mp}{n}$

29. $\dfrac{n^2}{m}$

27. _____

28. _____

30. Find the mean of the data: $-4, 8, -6, -12, 11, -16, 3, -9, 7$.

29. _____

Use the properties of addition and multiplication to find the missing number. Name the property.

30. _____

31. $6(8 \cdot 7) = (6 \cdot \underline{})(7)$

32. $1 \cdot 36 = 36 \cdot \underline{}$

31. _____

33. $13(18 - 6) = 13(18) - 13(\underline{})$ **34.** $9 + 11 + 8 = 9 + \underline{} + 11$

32. _____

33. _____

Simplify the expression.

34. _____

35. $9 \cdot x \cdot (-5)$

36. $(-28 + x) + (3x - 14)$

35. _____

37. $7x + 5y - 11x + 3y$

38. $6(x - 3) + 2x + 5$

36. _____

In Exercises 39–41, use the coordinate plane.

37. _____

39. Which point has coordinates of $(3, -2)$?

40. Describe the location of point B.

38. _____

41. What are the coordinates of point C?

39. _____

40. _____

41. _____

In Exercises 42–44, use the coordinate plane.

42. Plot and connect the points $A(1, 2)$, $B(-4, 2)$, $C(-4, -3)$, $D(1, -3)$.

42. _____See left.____

43. _____

44. _____

43. Identify the figure.

44. Find the perimeter of the figure.

Name _____ Date _____

Chapter Test C
For use after Chapter 2

Write a numerical expression for the verbal expression.

1. the opposite of negative twelve

2. the opposite of the absolute value of fifteen

3. the opposite of the absolute value of the sum of negative five and negative three

In Exercises 4–7, simplify the expression.

4. $-|-201|$

5. $-(-1|-28|)$

6. $-6 \cdot |-3| - (-5)$

7. $-|-12| + -(-8)$

8. Order the integers from least to greatest:
$|-12|, -21, -|-8|, -(-15), |23|, -|17|$

Find the sum or difference.

9. $-113 + 57 + (-206)$

10. $-3 - (-65) - 27$

11. $36 + (-87) + 1 - (-41)$

12. $-261 + |-72| - (-83) + (-15)$

Evaluate $-536 - x$ for the given value of x.

13. $x = -251$

14. $x = -|-715|$

In Exercises 15 and 16, solve the equation using mental math.

15. $-36 + x = 17$

16. $-15 = y + (-51)$

17. A weatherman keeps track of precipitation for the first six months of a year. His findings are summarized in the table below. How far above or below normal is the area's precipitation?

	Jan	Feb	Mar	Apr	May	June
Normal precipitation (in.)	8	6	5	7	5	3
Actual precipitation (in.)	9	4	7	3	4	5

Find the product or quotient.

18. $-11(-12)(-4)$

19. $-15 \cdot |-6| \cdot 7$

20. $\dfrac{-|-14|}{21}$

21. $\dfrac{-15}{-36}$

Answers

1. _____

2. _____

3. _____

4. _____

5. _____

6. _____

7. _____

8. _____

9. _____

10. _____

11. _____

12. _____

13. _____

14. _____

15. _____

16. _____

17. _____

18. _____

19. _____

20. _____

21. _____

Name _____ Date _____

Chapter Test C

For use after Chapter 2

22. Find the mean of the data:

$-14, 31, |-17|, -19, |22|, -41, -6, -|-30|$.

Evaluate the expression when $x = -7$, $y = -11$, and $z = 14$.

23. $(3y - 2x)^2$

24. $\dfrac{-z(yz - x^2)}{x}$

Simplify the expression.

25. $6a - 7b + 11 - 9a + 6b - 15$

26. $7(x - 3) - 3(x - 2y) + 8y$

27. $4(0.5x - 2.3y) + 1.3x - 4y$

28. $-3(3xy + 2x - 5y) + 5(2xy - 3x + 4y)$

29. You are buying four pairs of pants that cost $38 each. The store is having a special sale: buy one pair and get one at 50% off. How much will the four pairs of pants cost?

In Exercises 30–32, use the coordinate plane.

30. Plot and connect the points $A(4, -5)$, $B(-2, -5)$, $C(4, -1)$ and $D(-2, -1)$.

31. Find the perimeter of the rectangle.

32. Find the area of the rectangle.

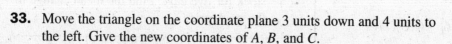

Answers

22. _____

23. _____

24. _____

25. _____

26. _____

27. _____

28. _____

29. _____

30. _____See left._____

31. _____

32. _____

33. _____

33. Move the triangle on the coordinate plane 3 units down and 4 units to the left. Give the new coordinates of A, B, and C.

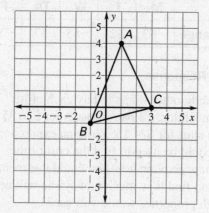

Standardized Test

For use after Chapter 2

Multiple Choice

1. Which of the following integers are in order from least to greatest?

(A) $0, 2, -4, 6, -8$

(B) $-7, -4, 1, 3, 11$

(C) $0, -8, -6, 7, 11$

(D) $-15, -18, 0, 5, 13$

2. Which of the following is not equal to $-|-15|$?

(F) $-(-15)$ (G) $-|15|$

(H) $-[-(-|-15|)]$ (I) $-(-(-15))$

3. Evaluate $-71 + (-53) + 41 + (-17)$.

(A) 66 (B) -100

(C) -182 (D) 100

4. What is the value of $-8 - (-11) + (-2) - 19$?

(F) -14 (G) -40

(H) -18 (I) -2

5. Evaluate $-b + 4ac$ when $a = 2$, $b = -5$, and $c = -8$.

(A) -69 (B) -5

(C) 69 (D) -59

6. What is the value of $|-6| \cdot (-5)(7)$?

(F) -31 (G) 210

(H) -210 (I) -29

7. Evaluate $\frac{-15y}{x}$ when $x = -9$ and $y = -3$.

(A) 45 (B) -45

(C) 5 (D) -5

8. Which of the following is equivalent to $8 - 6 + (-3) - (-7)$?

(F) $8 + 3 - 6 - 7$

(G) $2 + (-10)$

(H) $8 + 7 + (-3) + (-6)$

(I) $-3 + (-7) + 8 - 6$

9. Simplify the expression $3(4x - 5) - 8x - 4$.

(A) $4x - 19$ (B) $20x - 9$

(C) $4x - 9$ (D) $-x - 6$

10. Which point has coordinates $(2, -3)$?

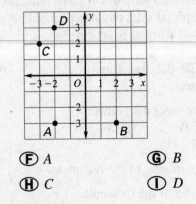

(F) A (G) B

(H) C (I) D

Short Response

11. The table shows the changes in the price of a stock for five days. Find the mean change in the stock price.

Day	M	T	W	Th	F
Price change	$-\$3$	$\$2$	$-\$5$	$\$7$	$-\$6$

Extended Response

12. A grandmother wants to buy each of her 7 grandchildren a pair of pants for \$36.35 and a shirt for \$24.15. Write an expression that could be used to find the cost of the clothing. Explain how you could use mental math to find how much money she will need. Which properties would you use?

Name _____ Date _____

Alternative Assessment and Math Journal

For use after Chapter 2

Journal

1. In your own words, describe what is meant by *like terms*. How do we add *like terms*? Give an example showing the use of the distributive property to add like terms.

Multi-Step Problem

2. The police are trying to catch a robbery suspect. They have a map of the city on the coordinate plane shown. On the map, each grid line represents a street.

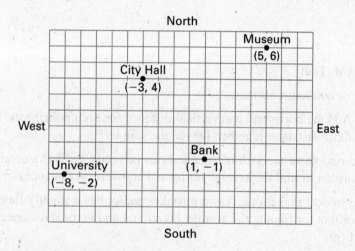

North

Museum (5, 6)

City Hall (−3, 4)

West   East

Bank (1, −1)

University (−8, −2)

South

a. The police station has coordinates (−5, 5). Add a point in the coordinate plane for the police station.

b. The thief wants to leave the bank and head to the museum. How many blocks east of the bank is the museum?

c. How many blocks north of the University is City Hall?

d. The mayor of the city is 3 blocks south and 6 blocks east of the bank. What are her coordinates?

e. A witness leaves the bank and heads 5 blocks north followed by 4 blocks west. What building is his new destination?

f. If the robber decides to head due east, which value will change: the *x*-coordinate or the *y*-coordinate? Will the coordinates increase or decrease?

g. If police officers are currently stationed at City Hall, the University, and the museum, explain how you could find the average number of blocks the three police officers would have to travel to get to the bank. (They can only travel on streets.)

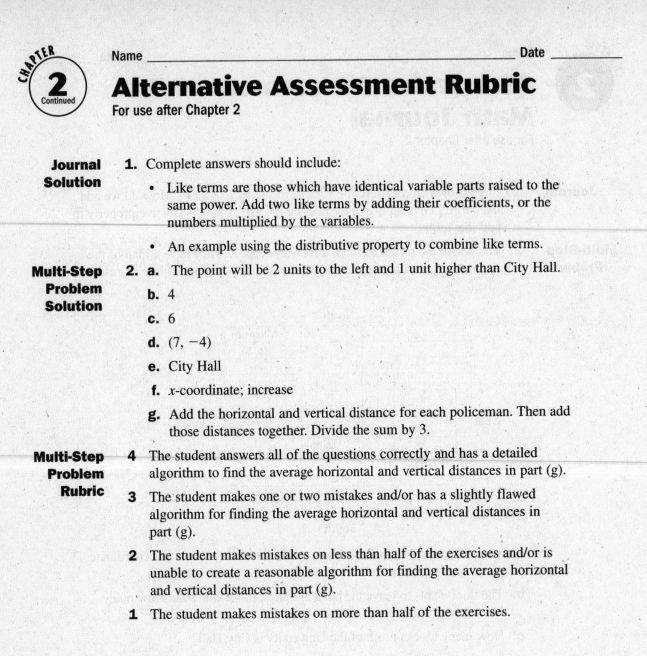

Alternative Assessment Rubric

For use after Chapter 2

**Journal
Solution**

1. Complete answers should include:

- Like terms are those which have identical variable parts raised to the same power. Add two like terms by adding their coefficients, or the numbers multiplied by the variables.

- An example using the distributive property to combine like terms.

**Multi-Step
Problem
Solution**

2. a. The point will be 2 units to the left and 1 unit higher than City Hall.

b. 4

c. 6

d. $(7, -4)$

e. City Hall

f. x-coordinate; increase

g. Add the horizontal and vertical distance for each policeman. Then add those distances together. Divide the sum by 3.

**Multi-Step
Problem
Rubric**

4 The student answers all of the questions correctly and has a detailed algorithm to find the average horizontal and vertical distances in part (g).

3 The student makes one or two mistakes and/or has a slightly flawed algorithm for finding the average horizontal and vertical distances in part (g).

2 The student makes mistakes on less than half of the exercises and/or is unable to create a reasonable algorithm for finding the average horizontal and vertical distances in part (g).

1 The student makes mistakes on more than half of the exercises.

Name _____ Date _____

Quiz 1
For use after Lessons 3.1–3.4

In Exercises 1–4, solve the equation.

Answers

1. $x - 26 = 12$

2. $21x = -147$

3. $\dfrac{y}{-12} = 6$

4. $8x - 15 = 73$

5. You walk dogs after school to earn spending money. You make $3 for each dog you walk. You earned $54 last week. Write and solve an equation to find the number of dogs you walked.

In Exercises 6 and 7, translate the statement into an equation. Then solve the equation.

6. The product of 6 and a number is 45.

7. The difference of 5 times a number and 3 is 22.

8. A pizza parlor charges $7.90 for a large pizza plus $1.25 for each additional topping. Write and solve an equation to find the number of extra toppings on a large pizza that costs $11.65.

1. _____

2. _____

3. _____

4. _____

5. _____

_____

6. _____

_____

7. _____

_____

8. _____

_____

Name _____ Date _____

Quiz 2
For use after Lessons 3.5–3.7

1. Find the area and perimeter of a rectangle with a width of 8 inches and a length of 15 inches.

Find the value of the variable in each figure.

2. $A = 64$ in.^{2}

3. $A = $ ^{2}

s

s

h

9 m

4. $P = 52$ ft

x

17 ft

In Exercises 5–8, solve the inequality. Then graph its solution.

5. $x - 8 < 16$

6. $-12 \geq t - 17$

7. $42 \geq 7t$

8. $-\frac{1}{3}a < 15$

Answers

1. _____

2. _____

3. _____

4. _____

5. _____

See left.

6. _____

See left.

7. _____

See left.

8. _____

See left.

9. _____

_____

10. _____

_____

9. A delivery truck weighs 2516 pounds when it is empty. When it is filled, it weighs more than 6700 pounds. Write and solve an inequality to find the weight of a full load.

10. You have $10 to spend at the fair. Write and solve an inequality to find how many rides you can go on if each ride costs $.75.

Chapter Test A

For use after Chapter 3

Describe an inverse operation that will undo the given operation.

Answers

1. Adding 7
2. Multiply by -9

Solve the equation.

3. $s + 6 = 14$
4. $21 = m - 11$
5. $x + 24 = 63$

6. $-11a = 121$
7. $\frac{y}{4} = 16$
8. $-\frac{1}{3}z = 5$

9. $2c + 4 = 6$
10. $5x - 14 = 21$
11. $\frac{m}{2} + 7 = 3$

12. At a fruit stand you buy 5 quarts of strawberries and spend $18.75. Use the verbal model to write an algebraic model. Then solve the equation.

$$\boxed{\begin{array}{c}\text{Quarts of}\\\text{Strawberries}\end{array}} \times \boxed{\begin{array}{c}\text{Cost per}\\\text{quart}\end{array}} = \boxed{\begin{array}{c}\text{Total}\\\text{cost}\end{array}}$$

In Exercises 13–15, use the following information.

You order a DVD movie out of a catalog for $23.50. After adding on shipping and handling charges, the total cost of the DVD is $27.25.

13. Write a verbal model for the situation.

14. Substitute numbers and variables in the verbal model to write an algebraic model.

15. Solve the algebraic model.

In Exercises 16–18, match the statement with the correct equation.

16. The product of twice a number and 6 is 36.   **A.** $2 + 6n = 36$

17. The sum of 2 and 6 times a number is 36.   **B.** $6(2n) = 36$

18. The difference of 6 and twice a number is 36.   **C.** $6 - 2n = 36$

19. You buy 3 bags of apples at the grocery store. You give the cashier a $10 bill and receive $3.25 back in change. How much does each bag of apples cost?

Answers

1. _____
2. _____
3. _____
4. _____
5. _____
6. _____
7. _____
8. _____
9. _____
10. _____
11. _____
12. _____
_____
13. ___See left.___
14. _____
15. _____
16. _____
17. _____
18. _____
19. _____

CHAPTER
3
Continued

Chapter Test A
For use after Chapter 3

Find the area and perimeter of the figure.

Answers

20.

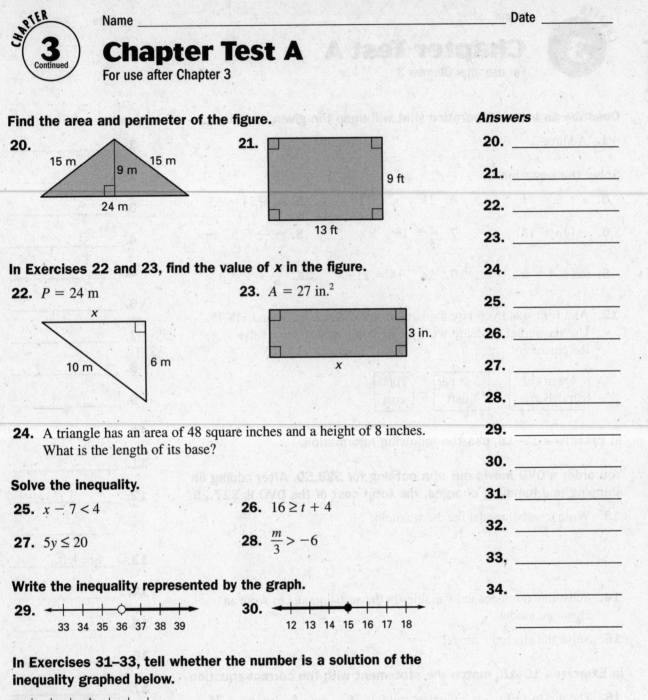

15 m   15 m
9 m
24 m

21.

9 ft
13 ft

In Exercises 22 and 23, find the value of x in the figure.

22. $P = 24$ m

x
10 m   6 m

23. $A = 27$ in.^{2}

3 in.
x

24. A triangle has an area of 48 square inches and a height of 8 inches. What is the length of its base?

Solve the inequality.

25. $x - 7 < 4$

26. $16 \geq t + 4$

27. $5y \leq 20$

28. $\frac{m}{3} > -6$

Write the inequality represented by the graph.

29.
33 34 35 36 37 38 39

30.
12 13 14 15 16 17 18

In Exercises 31–33, tell whether the number is a solution of the inequality graphed below.

−5 −4 −3 −2 −1 0 1

31. −4

32. 0

33. −2

34. You are buying two birthday gifts for friends and have $45 to spend. The first gift costs $21.35. Write and solve an inequality to determine how much you can spend on the second gift.

20. _____

21. _____

22. _____

23. _____

24. _____

25. _____

26. _____

27. _____

28. _____

29. _____

30. _____

31. _____

32. _____

33, _____

34. _____

Name _____ **Date** _____

Chapter Test B
For use after Chapter 3

In Exercises 1–9, solve the equation.

1. $52 = a - 16$

2. $m + 21 = 15$

3. $b + \dfrac{4}{9} = \dfrac{7}{9}$

4. $\dfrac{d}{8} = -23$

5. $13x = 91$

6. $2.3z = -9.2$

7. $13 = 29 - 8x$

8. $\dfrac{y}{15} + 4 = 21$

9. $4h - 7 = 41$

10. It costs \$120 to take 8 swimming lessons. Each lesson is an hour long and costs the same amount. How much is each lesson?

11. A rancher has 540 head of cattle. There are 117 calves in the herd. How many cattle were there before the calves were born?

In Exercises 12–14, translate the statement into an equation. Then solve the equation.

12. The quotient of 6 times a number and 10 is 3.

13. The sum of 16 and twice a number is 52.

14. The difference of a number multiplied by 4 and 11 is −3.

15. A white water rafting company charges \$65 for each raft rental. It also charges \$18 per person for life jacket rental, food, and portage back to the parking area. A group used one raft and their bill was \$209. Write and solve an equation to find the number of people in the group.

Answers

1. _____
2. _____
3. _____
4. _____
5. _____
6. _____
7. _____
8. _____
9. _____
10. _____
11. _____
12. _____

_____

13. _____

_____

14. _____

_____

15. _____

_____

Name _____ Date _____

Find the area and perimeter of the figure.

Answers

16.

11 m

13 m

17.

12 in.

11 in.   13 in.

6 in.

16. _____

17. _____

18. _____

19. _____

20. _____

21. _____

22. _____

23. _____

See left.

24. _____

See left.

25. _____

See left.

26. _____

18. Find the width of a rectangle with a length of 21 feet and a perimeter of 76 feet.

19. Find the base of a triangle with a height of 14 meters and an area of 112 square meters.

Write the inequality represented by the graph.

20.

  −14 −13 −12 −11 −10

21.

  5 6 7 8 9 10 11

In Exercises 22–24, solve the inequality. Then graph its solution.

22. $15 \le x + 18$

23. $\frac{1}{2}n > 6$

24. $-8m \ge 24$

25. You are running in gym class. You have 45 minutes and need to run 6 miles. Write and solve an inequality to find the amount of time you can spend running each mile.

26. You are going out with friends to see a movie and shop. You have $32 and the movie will cost $7.25. Write and solve an inequality to find how much money you can spend shopping.

Name _____ Date _____

Chapter Test C

For use after Chapter 3

In Exercises 1–8, solve the equation.

1. $-47 = x + 15$

2. $m - (-2.17) = -3.21$

3. $1.4 = 0.7p$

4. $\dfrac{x}{6.2} = -6$

5. $5x + 17 = -8$

6. $-\dfrac{x}{25} + 13 = 21$

7. $7\left(\dfrac{3}{7} + h\right) = 31$

8. $3(4 + x) + 5(2 - x) = 48$

9. You went to the grocery store and spent $9.70. You bought milk for $2.49, eggs for $.98, cereal for $3.98, and bananas. How much were the bananas?

10. A band is selling frozen pizzas to raise money for new uniforms. They get $1.50 profit for every pizza sold at $5.50. The band raised $834 for uniforms. How much were the total sales of the pizzas?

In Exercises 11–13, translate the statement into an equation. Then solve the equation.

11. Seven less than the product of 3 and a number is -16.

12. The sum of 18 times a number and -26 is 19.

13. The sum of 6 and 7, plus 5 times a number, is -12.

14. A baseball team's shirts cost $32 each. Also, there is a $1.25 per letter fee to have the student's last name stenciled on the back of the shirt. Write and solve an equation to determine how many letters are in a student's last name if his shirt costs $45.75.

15. You want to save $168 for a ski trip. You earn $6 an hour babysitting. You have already saved $45. Write and solve an equation to find the number of hours you need to babysit to earn the rest of the money.

Answers

1. _____
2. _____
3. _____
4. _____
5. _____
6. _____
7. _____
8. _____
9. _____
10. _____
11. _____
_____
12. _____
_____
13. _____
_____
14. _____
_____
15. _____
_____

16. A rectangle has a perimeter of 64 inches and a length of 18 inches. What is the width of the rectangle?

17. A triangle has an area of 42 square feet and a height of 14 feet. What is the length of the base?

18. A rectangle has an area of 104 square meters and a width of 8 meters. What is the perimeter of the rectangle?

19. Find the area of the shaded region in the figure.

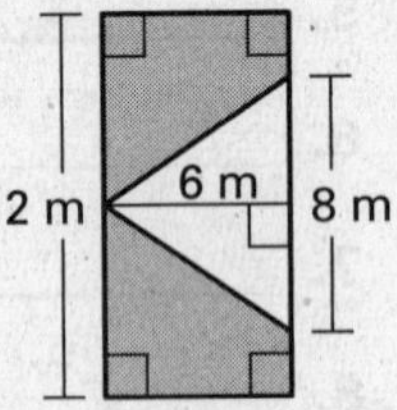

12 m   6 m   8 m

In Exercises 20–23, solve the inequality. Then graph its solution.

20. $5x - 11 \le 29$

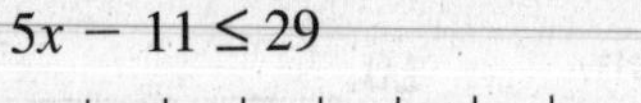

21. $15 - 3y > 57$

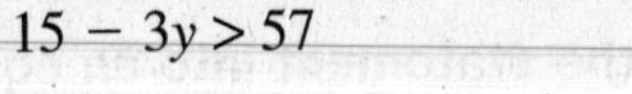

22. $-2(7 - x) \le -20$

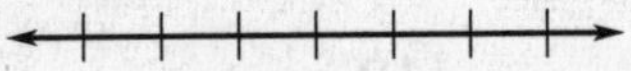

23. $7x - 12 \ge 6x - 13$

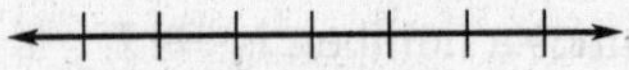

24. You are having a pool party and want to order 5 large pizzas. The pizza shop charges $3.75 for delivery. You have $58 to spend. Write and solve an inequality to determine the most money you can spend per pizza.

25. Your parents want to buy 3 dogs. They want to spend no more than $2000. Each dog will need a license for $15 and veterinary care for $100. Write and solve an inequality to find how much they can spend on each dog.

Answers

16. _____

17. _____

18. _____

19. _____

20. _____

      See left. _____

21. _____

      See left. _____

22. _____

      See left. _____

23. _____

      See left. _____

24. _____

25. _____

Name _____ Date _____

Standardized Test
For use after Chapter 3

1. Which equation is represented by the following statement?

The product of 6 and twice a number is 68.

(A) $6 + 2x = 68$ (B) $\frac{6}{2x} = 68$

(C) $6(2x) = 68$ (D) $6 - 2x = 68$

2. Solve $28 = t - 14$.

(F) 14   (G) 2   (H) 392   (I) 42

3. Which operation should you perform to solve the equation represented by the following statement?

The sum of x and $-$ is 2.

(A) Divide by -3 (B) Add 3

(C) Multiply by -3 (D) Subtract 3

4. Solve $\frac{1}{3}x = -15$.

(F) -18 (G) -12 (H) -45 (I) -5

5. Solve $-27 = 4x + 9$.

(A) 72   (B) -4.5 (C) 9   (D) -9

6. Which equation has the solution -8?

(F) $-3x - 8 = 16$ (G) $3x + 8 = -32$

(H) $-3x + 8 = 26$ (I) $3x - 8 = 16$

7. What is the width of a rectangle with a length of 6 feet and an area of 54 square feet?

(A) 21 feet   (B) 9 feet

(C) 18 feet   (D) 24 feet

8. Find the area of the triangle.

(F) 44 m^2

(G) 28 m^2

(H) 36 m^2

(I) 56 m^2

8 m   13 m   7 m

9. What value of m makes $-\frac{1}{2}m \geq 6$ true?

(A) -13 (B) -11 (C) 6   (D) 0

10. Which is the correct graph of $x > -3$?

(F) $\begin{array}{c} \longleftarrow\!\!+\!\!+\!\!+\!\!\circ\!\!+\!\!+\!\!+\!\!\longrightarrow \\ -6\ -5\ -4\ -3\ -2\ -1\ \ 0 \end{array}$

(G) $\begin{array}{c} \longleftarrow\!\!+\!\!+\!\!+\!\!\circ\!\!+\!\!+\!\!+\!\!\longrightarrow \\ -6\ -5\ -4\ -3\ -2\ -1\ \ 0 \end{array}$

(H) $\begin{array}{c} \longleftarrow\!\!+\!\!+\!\!+\!\!\bullet\!\!+\!\!+\!\!+\!\!\longrightarrow \\ -6\ -5\ -4\ -3\ -2\ -1\ \ 0 \end{array}$

(I) $\begin{array}{c} \longleftarrow\!\!+\!\!+\!\!+\!\!\bullet\!\!+\!\!+\!\!+\!\!\longrightarrow \\ -6\ -5\ -4\ -3\ -2\ -1\ \ 0 \end{array}$

Short Response

11. A plane flying at a constant speed travels 630 miles. It takes 4.5 hours to complete the trip. Write and solve an equation to find s, the plane's speed.

Extended Response

12. A kennel owner is buying a new building. He wants each dog run to be at least 96 square feet. The area reserved for the runs is 30 feet by 60 feet. Write and solve an inequality to show how many dog runs he can install that meet his requirements. Explain your answer.

Name _____ Date _____

Alternative Assessment and Math Journal

For use after Chapter 3

Journal

1. In your own words, discuss what the area and the perimeter of a triangle represent. For a triangle that has its sides and height given in centimeters, discuss what units you would use to express the area and perimeter.

Multi-Step Problem

2. A small lake contains a variety of fish species. A capture-and-release tagging program is used to estimate the population sizes of different types of fish in the lake.

a. You know that there are 225 catfish currently in the lake and that there were 30 more catfish in the lake a year ago. Let x represent the number of catfish in the lake last year. Write and solve an equation relating the number of catfish currently in the lake to the number in the lake last year.

b. There are 1.5 times more carp in the lake this year than last year. This year's carp population is 423. Write an equation to determine how many carp were in the lake last year. Solve the equation.

c. Next year the trout population is expected to be about 50 less than twice this year's population. Next year there are expected to be about 130 trout in the lake. Write an equation to determine how many trout are in the lake this year.

d. There are at least 80 pike in the lake. Write the number of pike in the lake as an inequality.

e. There are 200 bass in the lake. Four times the number of walleye in the lake is less than the number of bass in the lake. Write an inequality for the number of walleye in the lake. Solve the inequality.

f. Each year the number of turtles in the lake doubles. This year, there are between 60 and 80 turtles. In what range was the number of turtles two years ago?

g. Explain the difference in the solution set for a one-step equation such as $-5x = 100$ versus a one-step inequality such as $-5x < 100$.

Alternative Assessment Rubric

For use after Chapter 3

Journal Solution

1. Complete answers should include:

- The **perimeter** of a triangle is the sum of the lengths of the sides of the triangle.

- The **area** of a triangle is the amount of surface the triangle covers. The area of the triangle should be given in square centimeters. The perimeter of the triangle should be given in centimeters.

Multi-Step Problem Solution

2. a. $x - 30 = 225$; $x = 255$

b. $1.5c = 423$; $c = 282$

c. $2t - 50 = 130$; $t = 90$

d. $p \geq 80$

e. $4w < 200$; $w < 50$

f. Between 15 and 20

g. The answer to the one-step equation is a single value such as $x = -20$. The answer to the one-step inequality is a range of values such as $x > -20$.

Multi-Step Problem Rubric

4 The student correctly answers all of the problems and has a clearly stated answer to the writing question.

3 The student makes one or two mistakes in the problems and has an adequate answer to the writing exercise.

2 The student makes errors on up to half of the problems and/or does not have a clear or correct answer for the writing exercise.

1 The student makes errors on more than half of the problems.

UNIT 1

Unit 1 Test
For use after Chapters 1–3

Name _____ Date _____

Evaluate the expression.

1. $(7 + 8) \cdot 3 \div 5$

2. $4 \cdot 6 - 18 \div 2$

3. $(7 + 5)^2 \div 6$

4. $5 \cdot \left[12 + (3 + 4)^2\right]$

Write the statement as a variable expression. Let *x* represent the variable.

5. the quotient of a number and 11

6. 27 decreased by a number

In Exercises 7–10, solve the equation using mental math.

7. $\frac{x}{12} = 4$

8. $89 = 45 + y$

9. $w - 13 = 2$

10. $6b = 84$

11. Find the side length of a square that has an area of 196 square meters.

12. Find the side length of a square that has a perimeter of 52 feet.

Complete the statement with <, >, or =.

13. -7 ____ -11

14. 0 ____ -14

15. -11 ____ 6

16. $|12|$ ____ $|-12|$

17. $-|-1|$ ____ $-(-1)$

18. $-|8|$ ____ $|-8|$

Find the sum or difference.

19. $-76 + 51$

20. $-256 + (-172)$

21. $-87 - (-134)$

Find the product or quotient.

22. $-15(8)$

23. $-12(-6)(-4)$

24. $\frac{-104}{-8}$

Answers

1. _____
2. _____
3. _____
4. _____
5. _____
6. _____
7. _____
8. _____
9. _____
10. _____
11. _____
12. _____
13. _____
14. _____
15. _____
16. _____
17. _____
18. _____
19. _____
20. _____
21. _____
22. _____
23. _____
24. _____

Unit 1 Test
For use after Chapter 3

Answers

25. During one week, a person's stock portfolio changed by the following dollar values: $-125, 52, -71, 98, -64$. What was the mean change in the portfolio?

25. _____

Evaluate the expression when $x = -10$, $y = 9$, and $z = -6$.

26. $2x + 3yz$

27. $\dfrac{xy}{z}$

26. _____

27. _____

28. _____

Use the distributive property to evaluate the expression.

28. $-12(-1 + 8)$ 29. $7(-9 + 3)$ 30. $-3(5 - 14 - 6)$

29. _____

30. _____

Simplify the expression by combining like terms.

31. $17x - 8y - 9x - 3y$ 32. $5(2x + 8) - 3x - (-8x) - 21$

31. _____

32. _____

In Exercises 33 and 34, solve the equation.

33. $w + \dfrac{1}{6} = \dfrac{5}{6}$ 34. $21p = 231$

33. _____

34. _____

35. A tree is 110 inches tall. It grows 11 inches each year. Write and solve an equation to find how many years it will take to grow to 176 inches.

35. _____

36. Find the area of a triangle with a height of 12 inches and a base of 7 inches.

_____

Find the value of the variable in each figure.

36. _____

37. Perimeter = 60 cm

38. Area = 51 m²

37. _____

8 cm

6 m

38. _____

ℓ

b

39. _____

Solve the inequality.

40. _____

39. $-7.1 + w \ge -2.6$ 40. $4x < -124$

41. _____

41. $-2x > 32$ 42. $-\dfrac{1}{6}x \le -1$

42. _____

Name _____ Date _____

Cumulative Test

For use after Chapters 1–3

In Exercises 1 and 2, use the table that shows the average monthly hours a middle school computer lab was used by different grade levels.

Answers

1. Make a bar graph of the data.

Grade	Hours
5	11
6	17
7	13
8	22

2. Would a histogram be an appropriate way to display the data?

Evaluate the expression.

3. $2 \cdot 7 + 6 \cdot 5$ **4.** $10 - 4 + 15 \div 3$ **5.** $19 + 3 \cdot 6 - 4$

6. $36 \div [(19 - 16) \cdot 2]$ **7.** $7 \cdot (9 - 5)^3 + 16$ **8.** $13^2 - (4 + 7)^2 - 33$

In Exercises 9 and 10, evaluate the expression when $x = 6$ and $y = 3$.

9. $\dfrac{x^2}{3y}$

10. $\dfrac{7y - 3}{4x + 12}$

11. A pine tree that is 60 inches tall grows 8 inches per year. Write a variable expression for the height of the tree after y years.

In Exercises 12–15, solve the equation using mental math.

12. $7 + x = 22$ **13.** $69 = x - 17$ **14.** $17x = 68$ **15.** $\dfrac{33}{x} = 3$

16. It takes a squirrel 3 minutes to climb an oak tree, get an acorn, and carry it back to its nest. Write and solve an equation to find out how many acorns it can gather in an hour.

In Exercises 17 and 18, find the perimeter and area of the figure.

17.

8 in.

13 in.

18.

7 m

19. A bird is flying at a speed of 71.5 feet per second. How far does the bird travel in 6 seconds?

20. How far does an airplane travel in 3.5 hours at a rate of 560 miles per hour?

1. _____See left._____

2. _____

3. _____

4. _____

5. _____

6. _____

7. _____

8. _____

9. _____

10. _____

11. _____

12. _____

13. _____

14. _____

15. _____

16. _____

17. _____

18. _____

19. _____

20. _____

Name _____ Date _____

Cumulative Test

For use after Chapters 1–3

Write the next number in the pattern.

21. 2, 8, 32, 128, …   **22.** 243, 81, 27, 9, …

23. Jerry is saving money for a digital camera that costs \$290. He makes \$6.50 an hour working part-time at a bike shop, and has already saved \$134. Use the problem solving plan to find how many hours he needs to work to earn enough money for the camera.

24. Find $-|x|$ when $x = 6$ and when $x = -11$.

Order the integers from least to greatest.

25. $-37, 15, 9, -11, 0, -17$ **26.** $26, -64, -57, -96, 72$

Find the sum or difference.

27. $187 + (-109)$ **28.** $-76 + 24$ **29.** $-88 + (-37)$

30. $29 - 68$ **31.** $-17 - 31$ **32.** $52 - (-41)$

In Exercises 33–38, find the product or quotient.

33. $17(-21)$ **34.** $6(-11)(-8)$ **35.** $-1(-6)(-7)$

36. $\dfrac{36}{-2}$ **37.** $\dfrac{-8}{0}$ **38.** $\dfrac{-216}{-18}$

39. A sports store marked down each pair of ski boots by \$11. Write an expression to find the total change in selling prices where x is the number of pairs of ski boots remaining. If the store had 15 pairs of boots left, what was the total change?

40. Find the mean of the data: $11, -7, -8, 5, -13, -5, -9, 2$.

Answers

21. _____

22. _____

23. _____

24. _____
    _____

25. _____

26. _____

27. _____

28. _____

29. _____

30. _____

31. _____

32. _____

33. _____

34. _____

35. _____

36. _____

37. _____

38. _____

39. _____
    _____

40. _____

Name _____ Date _____

Cumulative Test

For use after Chapters 1-3

Use the properties of addition and multiplication to find the missing number. Name the property.

41. $17 + \underline{\quad} = 33 + 17$

42. $(10 + 4) + 21 = 10 + (\underline{\quad} + 21)$

43. $14 \cdot 25 = 25 \cdot \underline{\quad}$

44. $8(4 \cdot 2) = (8 \cdot 4)\underline{\quad}$

Use the distributive property to simplify the expression.

45. $9(6 - 7x)$

46. $6(11x + 8)$

Simplify the expression by combining like terms.

47. $7x + 9 - 11x + 6$

48. $3x - 5y - (-8x) + 14y$

Give the coordinates of the point and describe its location.

49. A **50.** B

51. C **52.** D

In Exercises 53–56, solve the equation.

53. $y + 27 = -11$

54. $3.6x = 19.44$

55. $8b + 35 = -29$

56. $42 = \dfrac{w}{-5} + 17$

57. A phone bill came to $40.27. There was a base fee of $29 per month, plus a $.23 per minute charge for long distance calls. Write and solve an equation to find the number of long distance minutes used.

58. You and your friends are going to a concert. You buy 9 tickets that are all the same price. The total charge for all the tickets is $252. Write and solve an equation to find the price of one concert ticket.

59. A waitress makes $7.50 per hour plus tips. For one day, she makes $92 in tips and earns a total of $137. Write and solve an equation to find the number of hours she worked.

Answers

41. _____

42. _____

_____

43. _____

_____

44. _____

_____

45. _____

46. _____

47. _____

48. _____

49. _____

50. _____

51. _____

52. _____

53. _____

54. _____

55. _____

56. _____

57. _____

_____

58. _____

_____

59. _____

Cumulative Test

For use after Chapters 1-3

In Exercises 60 and 61, translate the statement into an equation. Then solve the equation.

60. Twice a number, decreased by 7, is −11.

61. The sum of 3 times a number and −4 is 14.

62. Find the area and perimeter of the triangle.

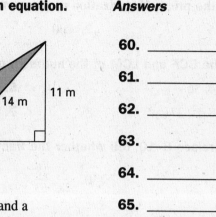

20 m

14 m

11 m

8 m

Find the unknown measure.

63. Find the width of a rectangle with a length of 15 inches and a perimeter of 46 inches.

64. Find the height of a triangle with a base that is 14 meters long and an area of 112 square meters.

65. Find the third side length of a triangle with a perimeter of 48 feet and two side lengths of 15 feet and 17 feet.

In Exercises 66–69, solve the inequality.

66. $27 > x + 18$

67. $31 - x \le 15$

68. $-\dfrac{1}{2}x > 2$

69. $15 \le 2x - 11$

70. You have $45 to spend on an outfit. You buy a pair of pants for $29.85. Write and solve an inequality to determine how much you can spend on a shirt to go with the pants.

Answers

60. _____

61. _____

62. _____

63. _____

64. _____

65. _____

66. _____

67. _____

68. _____

69. _____

70. _____

Name _____ Date _____

Quiz 1
For use after Lessons 4.1–4.4

Write the prime factorization of the number using exponents.

1. 56   **2.** 200   **3.** 180

Find the GCF and LCM of the numbers or variable expressions.

4. 24, 36   **5.** 38, 50

6. $18xz^2, 27x^2y$ **7.** $10xy^2, 15x^2y$

In Exercises 8–10, tell whether the fractions are equivalent.

8. $\dfrac{9}{15}, \dfrac{12}{20}$ **9.** $\dfrac{8}{28}, \dfrac{18}{63}$ **10.** $\dfrac{15}{45}, \dfrac{20}{49}$

11. Halie and Nina are running laps around the outside of their house.
They both start at the front door at the same time. Halie takes
18 seconds to run all the way around. Nina takes 20 seconds.
If they maintain the same speed, how long will it be before they are
both at the front door at the same time again?

Answers

1. _____

2. _____

3. _____

4. _____

5. _____

6. _____

7. _____

8. _____

9. _____

10. _____

11. _____

Name _____ Date _____

Quiz 2
For use after Lessons 4.5–4.8

Complete the statement with <, >, or =.

Answers

1. $\dfrac{24}{30}$ ___ $\dfrac{18}{24}$ 　　**2.** $\dfrac{9}{12}$ ___ $\dfrac{15}{20}$ 　　**3.** $\dfrac{3}{8}$ ___ $\dfrac{8}{17}$

Order the numbers from least to greatest.

4. $1\dfrac{11}{18},\ 1\dfrac{7}{9},\ \dfrac{8}{5},\ 1\dfrac{11}{15}$ 　　**5.** $-2\dfrac{3}{8},\ -\dfrac{9}{4},\ -2\dfrac{3}{7},\ -2\dfrac{5}{14}$

Multiply or divide. Write your answer using only positive exponents.

6. $w^8 \cdot w^6$ 　　**7.** $\dfrac{d^{11}}{d^5}$

8. $m^{-12} \cdot m^9 \cdot m^0$ 　　**9.** $\dfrac{x^5}{x^{-7}}$

Write the number in scientific notation.

10. 8,617,000 　　**11.** 0.0000005716

Answers

1. _____
2. _____
3. _____
4. _____
5. _____
6. _____
7. _____
8. _____
9. _____
10. _____
11. _____

Name _____ Date _____

Chapter Test A

For use after Chapter 4

Write all the factors of the number.

1. 24 **2.** 52

Write the prime factorization of the number.

3. 36 **4.** 75

In Exercises 5–7, find the greatest common factor of the numbers.

5. 15, 20 **6.** 30, 48 **7.** 300, 360

8. At the local fair, one barn is displaying chickens and rabbits. There are 140 chickens and 160 rabbits. Each animal is in its own cage. The cages will be arranged in equal rows without mixing animal types. What is the greatest number of animals that can be in each row?

Write the fraction in simplest form.

9. $\frac{25}{35}$ **10.** $\frac{14}{21}$ **11.** $\frac{45a^2}{65a}$

In Exercises 12 and 13, tell whether the fractions are equivalent.

12. $\frac{24}{36}, \frac{30}{45}$ **13.** $\frac{24}{40}, \frac{12}{21}$

14. Evaluate the expression $\frac{10x^4}{15x}$ when $x = 3$.

Find the least common multiple of the numbers.

15. 15, 40 **16.** 14, 21 **17.** 30, 70

Find the least common multiple of the monomials.

18. $4ab^2, 6a^2b$ **19.** $10x^3y, 25x^2y^2$

Answers

1. _____
2. _____
3. _____
4. _____
5. _____
6. _____
7. _____
8. _____
9. _____
10. _____
11. _____
12. _____
13. _____
14. _____
15. _____
16. _____
17. _____
18. _____
19. _____

Complete the statement with <, >, or =.

20. $\dfrac{6}{12}$ ——— $\dfrac{13}{24}$ **21.** $1\dfrac{5}{7}$ ——— $\dfrac{36}{21}$ **22.** $\dfrac{7}{9}$ ——— $\dfrac{11}{12}$

Order the numbers from least to greatest.

23. $\dfrac{3}{14}, \dfrac{2}{7}, \dfrac{1}{6}$ **24.** $1\dfrac{3}{4}, 1\dfrac{2}{3}, 1\dfrac{1}{2}, 1\dfrac{5}{12}$

Simplify the expression. Write your answer as a power.

25. $5^3 \cdot 5^6$ **26.** $b^7 \cdot b^{11}$ **27.** $\dfrac{c^{12}}{c^8}$

Evaluate the expression.

28. 5^{-2} **29.** $(-3)^0$ **30.** $2^{-6} \cdot 2^2$

Simplify. Write the expression using only positive exponents.

31. $a^{-6} \cdot a^4$ **32.** $\dfrac{b^{-3}}{b^7}$

Write the number in scientific notation.

33. 2,140,000   **34.** 0.000189

Write the number in standard form.

35. 6.71×10^{-5} **36.** 3.24×10^4

Answers

20. _____

21. _____

22. _____

23. _____

24. _____

25. _____

26. _____

27. _____

28. _____

29. _____

30. _____

31. _____

32. _____

33. _____

34. _____

35. _____

36. _____

Name _____ Date _____

Chapter Test B

For use after Chapter 4

Write all the factors of the number. Then tell whether the number is prime or composite.

1. 68   **2.** 110   **3.** 31

Write the prime factorization of the number.

4. 70   **5.** 360

In Exercises 6–8, find the GCF of the numbers or variable expressions.

6. 72, 84   **7.** 24, 52, 68   **8.** $24x^2y$, $30xyz$

9. A farmer is planting tomatoes, cucumbers, and peppers. He has 420 tomato plants, 546 pepper plants, and 462 cucumber plants. The plants will be arranged in equal rows without mixing plant types. What is the greatest number of plants he can put in each row?

Simplify.

10. $\dfrac{12}{21}$ **11.** $\dfrac{5x^2y}{25xy^2}$ **12.** $\dfrac{-36ab^3}{9a^2b}$

Write two fractions that are equivalent to the given fraction.

13. $\dfrac{27}{63}$ **14.** $\dfrac{5}{9}$

In Exercises 15–18, find the LCM.

15. 45, 60, 90   **16.** 15, 21, 25

17. $6xz^2$, $21y^2z$ **18.** $15a^2b^2c$, $30abc^3$

19. Newborn twins fall asleep at 8:00 P.M. The first twin wakes up for a bottle every 60 minutes, then goes back to sleep. The second twin wakes up for a bottle every 80 minutes. How long after 8:00 P.M. do both twins wake up at the same time?

Answers

1. _____
2. _____
3. _____
   _____
4. _____
5. _____
6. _____
7. _____
8. _____
9. _____
10. _____
11. _____
12. _____
13. _____
14. _____
15. _____
16. _____
17. _____
18. _____
19. _____

Chapter Test B

For use after Chapter 4

Complete the statement with <, >, or =.

20. $\dfrac{9}{25}$ ——— $\dfrac{31}{100}$ **21.** $1\dfrac{2}{7}$ ——— $\dfrac{27}{21}$ **22.** $\dfrac{10}{27}$ ——— $\dfrac{31}{100}$

Order the numbers from least to greatest.

23. $\dfrac{2}{3}, \dfrac{4}{9}, \dfrac{11}{12}, \dfrac{5}{6}$ **24.** $-1\dfrac{1}{3}, -\dfrac{5}{4}, -1\dfrac{4}{7}, -1\dfrac{3}{8}$

Simplify the expression. Write your answer as a power.

25. $m^{12} \cdot m^5$ **26.** $\dfrac{n^{15}}{n^{11}}$ **27.** $\dfrac{3^4 a^5}{3^2 a^2}$

Evaluate the expression.

28. $3^{-12} \cdot 3^8$ **29.** $6 \cdot 6^{-3}$ **30.** $11^{-1} \cdot 11^3 \cdot 11^{-2}$

In Exercises 31–33, simplify the expression using only positive exponents.

31. $a^6 \cdot a^{-4} \cdot a^{-3}$ **32.** $\dfrac{6b^{-3}}{2b^4}$ **33.** $c^{-2} \cdot c^7 \cdot c^{-8}$

34. As of the year 2000, Earth's population was estimated to be 6,200,000,000. Write this number in scientific notation.

Write the product in scientific notation.

35. $(8 \times 10^5) \times (6 \times 10^8)$

36. $(7.2 \times 10^4) \times (5.1 \times 10^6)$

Answers

20. _____

21. _____

22. _____

23. _____

24. _____

25. _____

26. _____

27. _____

28. _____

29. _____

30. _____

31. _____

32. _____

33. _____

34. _____

35. _____

36. _____

Name _____ Date _____

Chapter Test C

For use after Chapter 4

Write the prime factorization of the number using exponents.

1. 300   **2.** 882   **3.** 4725

In Exercises 4–7, find the GCF of the variable expressions.

4. $25w^2u, 30wu^4$ **5.** $36x^2yz^4, 78x^3y^2z^2$

6. $39a^6bc^9, 24abc^5$ **7.** $36v^2u^3w, 18v^3u^5w^2, 24vu^4$

8. A grocery store clerk is arranging cans of vegetables on shelves. There are 150 cans of beets, 240 cans of corn, 210 cans of peas, and 180 cans of green beans. The cans will be arranged in equal rows without mixing vegetable types. What is the greatest number of cans that can be in a row?

Tell whether the fractions are equivalent.

9. $\dfrac{121}{132}, \dfrac{66}{72}$ **10.** $\dfrac{9ab^2}{12ab}, \dfrac{15a^2b}{20a}$ **11.** $\dfrac{14a^3b}{18ab^3}, \dfrac{21a^2b^5}{27b^7}$

In Exercises 12–15, find the LCM.

12. 84, 126, 140   **13.** 105, 525, 945

14. $16a^3bc^4, 17b^3c$ **15.** $36x^5z^2, 15y^2z^4$

16. There are two cheetahs in an enclosure. Both cheetahs come out of their den and begin pacing the perimeter of their enclosure at the same time. The male cheetah takes 150 seconds to pace the perimeter. The female takes 210 seconds. If they maintain the same speed, how many seconds will it take before both are at the den opening at the same time again?

Answers

1. _____

2. _____

3. _____

4. _____

5. _____

6. _____

7. _____

8. _____

9. _____

10. _____

11. _____

12. _____

13. _____

14. _____

15. _____

16. _____

Name _____ Date _____

Chapter Test C

For use after Chapter 4

Complete the statement with <, >, or =.

17. $\dfrac{11}{16}$ —— $\dfrac{23}{34}$ **18.** $\dfrac{19}{40}$ —— $\dfrac{34}{67}$ **19.** $1\dfrac{13}{17}$ —— $\dfrac{90}{51}$

Order the numbers from least to greatest.

20. $\dfrac{9}{6},\ 1\dfrac{4}{9},\ 1\dfrac{5}{18},\ \dfrac{4}{3}$ **21.** $-\dfrac{17}{24},\ -\dfrac{2}{3},\ -\dfrac{5}{6},\ -\dfrac{7}{8}$

Simplify the expression. Write your answer as a power.

22. $3x^2y^4 \cdot 3xy^5$ **23.** $6^2a^6b^7c \cdot 6^3a^2b^9c^2$

24. $\dfrac{7^4\,w^4\,v^5}{7^3\,w^7\,v^4}$ **25.** $\left(\dfrac{5^5}{5^2}\right)^3$

Simplify the expression using only positive exponents.

26. $\dfrac{27x^{-6}}{6x^{-4}}$ **27.** $3^2a^{-4}b \cdot 3^{-4}a^2b^{-3}$

28. $\dfrac{-8u^6\,v^{-2}}{4u^2\,v^5}$ **29.** $\dfrac{-6^2\,m^{-3}\,n^4 \cdot 6^{-3}\,m^4\,n^{-2}}{6^{-1}mn^2}$

In Exercises 30 and 31, find the missing exponent.

30. $36a = \dfrac{6^{-2}\,a^4}{6^?\,a^3}$ **31.** $\dfrac{x^{-8}}{x^?} = x^6$

32. In 2000, the population of Florida was about 15,982,000. Write this number in scientific notation.

Write the product or quotient in scientific notation.

33. $\left(4.7 \times 10^{15}\right) \times \left(3.8 \times 10^6\right) \times \left(1.3 \times 10^{-4}\right)$

34. $\dfrac{6.72 \times 10^{15}}{4.2 \times 10^9}$

Answers

17. _____

18. _____

19. _____

20. _____

21. _____

22. _____

23. _____

24. _____

25. _____

26. _____

27. _____

28. _____

29. _____

30. _____

31. _____

32. _____

33. _____

34. _____

Name _____ Date _____

Standardized Test

For use after Chapter 4

---

1. What is the prime factorization of 700?

   A $7 \cdot 10^2$ **B** $2^2 \cdot 5^2 \cdot 7$

   C $2^2 \cdot 7^2 \cdot 5$ **D** $4 \cdot 5^2 \cdot 7$

2. What is the GCF of 210 and 180?

   F 30   **G** 60   **H** 90   **I** 1260

3. Which pair of fractions are equivalent?

   A $\frac{6}{9}, \frac{13}{15}$ **B** $\frac{7}{15}, \frac{20}{44}$

   C $\frac{11}{25}, \frac{7}{16}$ **D** $\frac{4}{6}, \frac{10}{15}$

4. Which fraction is in simplest form?

   F $\frac{35}{40}$ **G** $\frac{12}{18}$ **H** $\frac{15}{17}$ **I** $\frac{6}{9}$

5. A nurse volunteers at a health clinic every 9 days. Her friend volunteers at the same clinic every 6 days. If they work together today, how many days will it be before they work together again?

   A 3   **B** 6   **C** 9   **D** 18

6. Find the LCM of $16x^3$ and $40x^5$.

   F $80x^5$ **G** $40x^5$ **H** $8x^3$ **I** $80x^8$

7. Which statement is true?

   A $\frac{14}{10} > 1\frac{24}{36}$ **B** $-\frac{17}{25} > -\frac{3}{4}$

   C $\frac{8}{13} < \frac{12}{25}$ **D** $-\frac{3}{8} < -\frac{15}{32}$

8. Simplify $5^2 m^3 n^2 \cdot 5m^6 n^4$.

   F $125m^{18}n^8$ **G** $125m^9 n^6$

   H $5m^{-3}n^{-2}$ **I** $25m^9 n^6$

9. Write $\dfrac{10x^{-9}}{-5x^2}$ using only positive exponents.

   A $-2x^{11}$ **B** $\dfrac{1}{2x^7}$ **C** $\dfrac{-2}{x^7}$ **D** $\dfrac{-2}{x^{11}}$

10. Write 3,670,000,000 in scientific notation.

    F 367×10^7 **G** 3.67×10^9

    H 3.67×10^{-9} **I** 367×10^{-7}

11. Simplify $(6.1 \times 10^{-9}) \times (2.3 \times 10^3)$.

    A 1.403×10^{-5} **B** 1.403×10^{-6}

    C 14.03×10^{-6} **D** 1.403×10^{-7}

Short Response

12. A music teacher is arranging 32 students in a rectangular group for a concert. He wants the same number of students in each row. List the ways he can arrange the students. Which arrangements are the better choices? Why?

Extended Response

13. A store clerk is displaying CDs on a shelf. There are 150 pop, 210 rock, and 90 country CDs. The CDs will be arranged in equal rows without mixing music types. What is the greatest number of CDs that can be put in each row? Explain how you found your answer.

Name _____ Date _____

Alternative Assessment and Math Journal

For use after Chapter 4

Journal

1. Explain what it means for a whole number to either be *prime* or *composite*. Given two whole numbers, explain how to find the greatest common factor. What does it mean for two whole numbers to be *relatively prime*?

Multi-Step Problem

2. You can use Newton's Universal Law of Gravitation to write a formula to approximate the mass of the Earth. The formula for e, the mass of Earth in kilograms, is

$$e = fr^2g^{-1}$$

where f is the force, r is the radius of Earth, and g is the gravitational constant. f, r, and g have the numerical values $f = 9.8$, $r = 6.37 \times 10^6$, and $g = 6.67 \times 10^{-11}$.

a. Rewrite the value of r in standard form.

b. Rewrite the value of g in standard form.

c. Write f, r, and g in order from least to greatest.

d. Rewrite the formula for e without negative exponents.

e. Using your formula for e, calculate the mass of Earth. The answer you get will be in kilograms.

f. To compute the density d of Earth, you can use the formula $d = v^{-1}e$ where v is the volume of Earth. Write the density formula without negative exponents.

g. The volume of Earth is approximately $v = 1.11 \times 10^{27}$ cm^3. Use your results from parts (e) and (f) to find the density of Earth. Give your answer using scientific notation.

h. Write your answer for the density of Earth in standard form.

i. *Writing* Explain how your answer in part (e) for the mass of Earth would change if you were asked to give your answer in grams instead of kilograms.

Journal Solution

1. Complete answers should include:

   - A **prime** number is a whole number whose only factors are 1 and the number itself. A **composite** number is a whole number which has at least one factor other than 1 and the number itself. To find the greatest common factor of two whole numbers, write the prime factorization of each. The greatest common factor is the product of the common factors in each prime factorization. Two whole numbers are said to be relatively prime if their greatest common factor is 1.

Multi-Step Problem Solution

2. a. 6,370,000

   b. 0.0000000000667

   c. g, f, r

   d. $e = fr^2/g$

   e. 5.96×10^{24} kg

   f. $d = e/v$

   g. 5.37×10^3 kg/cm^3

   h. 0.00537 kg/cm^3

   i. You would convert the mass to grams by multiplying it by 1000 g/1 kg. This would give 5.96×10^{27} g.

Multi-Step Problem Rubric

4 The student correctly computes the mass and density of Earth, rewrites the formulas without negative exponents, and is able to convert between standard form and scientific notation.

3 The student makes the computations, rewrites the formulas, and converts between standard form and scientific notation with at most 2 errors.

2 The student makes the computations, rewrites the formulas, and converts between standard form and scientific notation with at most 4 errors.

1 The student has more than 4 errors in the calculations, rewriting of formulas, and numerical conversions.

CHAPTER 5

Name _____ Date _____

Quiz 1

For use after Lessons 5.1–5.4

In Exercises 1–6, find the sum or difference. Then simplify, if possible.

Answers

1. $\dfrac{5}{7} - \dfrac{3}{7}$

2. $1\dfrac{3}{8} + \dfrac{7}{8}$

3. $\dfrac{4x}{15} + \dfrac{7x}{15}$

4. $\dfrac{3}{4} + \dfrac{4}{5}$

5. $\dfrac{3x}{6} + \dfrac{x}{4}$

6. $3\dfrac{2}{3} - 1\dfrac{1}{5}$

7. You are making a salad with mixed greens. You use $2\dfrac{1}{4}$ pounds of iceberg lettuce and $1\dfrac{1}{6}$ pounds of romaine lettuce. You eat $\dfrac{2}{3}$ pound of the salad. How many pounds of salad are left?

In Exercises 8–13, find the product or quotient. Then simplify, if possible.

8. $\dfrac{9}{20} \cdot \dfrac{5}{8}$

9. $-\dfrac{14}{15} \cdot 1\dfrac{3}{7}$

10. $-6 \cdot \left(-2\dfrac{2}{3}\right)$

11. $\dfrac{2}{3} \div \dfrac{4}{9}$

12. $\dfrac{3}{8} \div \dfrac{2}{9}$

13. $2\dfrac{4}{5} \div (-7)$

14. During a thunderstorm, rain is falling at a rate of $\dfrac{3}{4}$ inch per hour. It rains at that rate for $3\dfrac{1}{5}$ hours. How much rain fell?

Answers

1. _____
2. _____
3. _____
4. _____
5. _____
6. _____
7. _____
8. _____
9. _____
10. _____
11. _____
12. _____
13. _____
14. _____

Name _____ Date _____

Quiz 2
For use after Lessons 5.5–5.8

Write the fraction as a decimal.

1. $\frac{3}{8}$ **2.** $\frac{5}{6}$

Write the decimal as a fraction in simplest form.

3. 0.64   **4.** $0.\overline{6}$

Find the sum or difference.

5. $17.36 + 23.951$ **6.** $-7.5 + 13.42$

7. $28.503 - 15.62$ **8.** $1.7 - (-3.05)$

In Exercises 9–12, find the product or quotient.

9. $2.31 \cdot (-1.2)$ **10.** $0.52 \cdot 4.8$

11. $4.125 \div 1.5$ **12.** $-1.152 \div 0.32$

13. Your mom is buying carnations to put in a flower arrangement. Each carnation costs $.69. If she has $15.25 to spend, how many carnations can she buy?

14. Find the mean, median, mode(s), and range of the data: 36, 28, 31, 39, 34, 36, 27.

Answers

1. _____

2. _____

3. _____

4. _____

5. _____

6. _____

7. _____

8. _____

9. _____

10. _____

11. _____

12. _____

13. _____

14. _____

_____

_____

_____

_____

Find the sum or difference. Then simplify, if possible.

Answers

1. $\dfrac{11}{13} + \dfrac{5}{13}$

2. $\dfrac{7}{16} - \dfrac{5}{16}$

3. $\dfrac{2c}{9} + \dfrac{4c}{9}$

4. $\dfrac{2}{3} + \left(-\dfrac{1}{6}\right)$

5. $-1\dfrac{3}{8} + \left(-3\dfrac{3}{4}\right)$

6. $-2\dfrac{2}{5} - \left(-3\dfrac{4}{15}\right)$

In Exercises 7–9, use the following information. You have three days to complete a 30-mile hike through Mount Rushmore National Park. You hike $8\dfrac{2}{3}$ miles the first day, and $11\dfrac{3}{5}$ miles the second day. How many miles will you have to hike the third day to finish the trip?

7. Write a verbal model to describe the problem.

8. Substitute the given values into the model.

9. Solve the equation to find the miles left to hike.

In Exercises 10–15, find the product or quotient.

10. $\dfrac{3}{5} \cdot \dfrac{5}{6}$

11. $\dfrac{3}{7} \cdot \left(-\dfrac{2}{9}\right)$

12. $-8 \cdot \left(-2\dfrac{1}{5}\right)$

13. $-\dfrac{8}{9} \div \dfrac{5}{6}$

14. $\dfrac{12}{15} \div 3$

15. $3\dfrac{2}{5} \div 2\dfrac{5}{6}$

16. During a hot week, a swimming pool lost $\dfrac{5}{8}$ inch of water each day due to evaporation. How much water evaporated by the end of seven days?

1. _____

2. _____

3. _____

4. _____

5. _____

6. _____

7. _____See left.____

8. _____

9. _____

10. _____

11. _____

12. _____

13. _____

14. _____

15. _____

16. _____

Name _____ Date _____

Chapter Test A
For use after Chapter 5

Write the fraction or mixed number as a decimal.

17. $\frac{1}{8}$ **18.** $\frac{2}{3}$ **19.** $3\frac{1}{4}$

In Exercises 20–22, write the decimal as a fraction or mixed number in simplest form.

20. -0.16 **21.** -5.05 **22.** $0.\overline{45}$

23. The data below are the weights of four gold finches. Order the numbers from least to greatest.

3.21 ounces, $3\frac{1}{4}$ ounces, 3.09 ounces, $3\frac{1}{5}$ ounces

Find the sum or difference.

24. $2.46 + 5.13$ **25.** $6.71 + 5.08$

26. $9.6 - 7.7$ **27.** $17.3 - 9.72$

In Exercises 28 and 29, solve the equation.

28. $x + 3.5 = 7.3$ **29.** $y - 8.12 = -9.36$

30. You are shopping and pick up four items that cost $2.76, $4.55, $3.30, and $5.48. Use front-end estimation to estimate the sum.

In Exercises 31–34, find the product or quotient.

31. $5.2 \cdot 1.9$ **32.** $-6.12 \cdot 0.8$

33. $-15.96 \div 3.8$ **34.** $-1.17 \div (-0.45)$

35. A leaking swimming pool loses about 4.6 gallons of water every hour for 8.5 hours. How many gallons of water did it lose?

36. Find the mean, median, mode(s), and range of the data:
7, -3, 6, -2, 8, 7, -4, 5, 3.

Answers

17. _____

18. _____

19. _____

20. _____

21. _____

22. _____

23. _____

24. _____

25. _____

26. _____

27. _____

28. _____

29. _____

30. _____

31. _____

32. _____

33. _____

34. _____

35. _____

36. _____

_____

_____

_____

Name _____ Date _____

Chapter Test B

For use after Chapter 5

Find the sum or difference. Then simplify, if possible.

1. $\frac{17}{19} + \frac{15}{19}$

2. $\frac{11}{12} - \frac{5}{12}$

3. $\frac{3}{5} + \frac{2}{3}$

4. $1\frac{7}{8} - 1\frac{3}{4}$

5. $-3\frac{3}{4} + \left(-2\frac{1}{3}\right)$

6. $-4\frac{4}{7} - \left(-5\frac{5}{14}\right)$

In Exercises 7–9, simplify the expression.

7. $\frac{2a}{15} + \frac{6a}{15}$

8. $-\frac{12b}{21} + \frac{8b}{21}$

9. $-\frac{7c}{9} - \left(-\frac{4c}{9}\right)$

10. The track team practiced for $2\frac{1}{4}$ hours on Monday, $1\frac{3}{8}$ hours on Tuesday, and $1\frac{11}{16}$ hours on Wednesday. How many hours did they practice in the three days?

In Exercises 11–16, find the product or quotient.

11. $\frac{3}{7} \cdot \frac{5}{8}$

12. $-4 \cdot \left(-\frac{11}{15}\right)$

13. $2\frac{2}{3} \cdot \left(-1\frac{3}{4}\right)$

14. $\frac{7}{12} \div \frac{3}{4}$

15. $-2\frac{4}{5} \div 8$

16. $-4\frac{1}{6} \div \left(-1\frac{3}{8}\right)$

17. A car travels $25\frac{1}{2}$ miles and uses one gallon of gasoline. If it has $2\frac{2}{3}$ gallons in the tank, how far can it travel before it runs out of gas?

Evaluate the expression when $a = -\frac{5}{6}$ **and** $b = 2\frac{2}{7}$.

18. $-6a$

19. ab

Answers

1. _____
2. _____
3. _____
4. _____
5. _____
6. _____
7. _____
8. _____
9. _____
10. _____
11. _____
12. _____
13. _____
14. _____
15. _____
16. _____
17. _____
18. _____
19. _____

Name _____ Date _____

Chapter Test B
For use after Chapter 5

Write the fraction or mixed number as a decimal.

20. $\frac{16}{25}$ **21.** $\frac{1}{15}$ **22.** $7\frac{5}{16}$

In Exercises 23–25, write the decimal as a fraction or mixed number.

23. 3.95   **24.** $0.\overline{8}$ **25.** 0.375

26. Order the numbers from least to greatest:
$5\frac{2}{7}$, 5.26, $5\frac{4}{15}$, $5\frac{1}{4}$, 5.3.

In Exercises 27–30, find the sum, difference, product or quotient.

27. $24.721 - 30.26$ **28.** $-7.971 + (-8.12)$

29. $5.61 \cdot 1.3$ **30.** $-2.546 \div 2.68$

31. You spend $12.65 on 4.6 pounds of dog food. How much was each pound of dog food?

In Exercises 32–35, solve the equation.

32. $x + (-7.21) = 4.6$ **33.** $5.8 + y = 2.7$

34. $\frac{w}{2.7} = 3.6$ **35.** $1.9z = 4.37$

36. A train travels 250.25 miles in 3.5 hours. Find the average speed, in miles per hour.

37. Find the mean, median, mode(s), and range of the data:
40, 42, 38, 35, 41, 33, 38, 43, 41.

Answers

20. _____

21. _____

22. _____

23. _____

24. _____

25. _____

26. _____

27. _____

28. _____

29. _____

30. _____

31. _____

32. _____

33. _____

34. _____

35. _____

36. _____

37. _____

_____

_____

_____

Chapter Test C
For use after Chapter 5

Evaluate.

Answers

1. $-\frac{5}{6} - \left(-\frac{2}{9}\right)$

2. $2\frac{3}{8} - 1\frac{5}{16} + 1\frac{1}{4}$

3. $3\frac{2}{3} - 4\frac{1}{6} - \left(-2\frac{3}{4}\right)$

4. $2\frac{3}{5} - \left(1\frac{1}{2} + 3\frac{3}{4}\right)$

Simplify the variable expression.

5. $-\frac{7x}{24} + \frac{11x}{24}$

6. $-\frac{4p}{15q} - \frac{7p}{15q}$

7. $\frac{5a}{14b} + \frac{7a}{21b}$

8. $\frac{2n}{3} - \frac{5n}{9} + \frac{5n}{6}$

Solve the equation.

9. $x + \frac{3}{7} = \frac{5}{7}$

10. $y - \frac{4}{5} = \frac{3}{10}$

11. $3\frac{5}{6} + 2\frac{1}{9} - w = 2\frac{5}{12}$

12. $z + 1\frac{2}{5} - 3\frac{2}{3} = 4\frac{1}{2}$

Find the product or quotient.

13. $\frac{5}{18} \cdot \frac{8}{15}$

14. $-\frac{7}{12} \div 21$

15. $\left(-1\frac{1}{8}\right) \cdot 4\frac{2}{3}$

16. $4\frac{1}{5} \div \left(-2\frac{5}{8}\right)$

In Exercises 17 and 18, evaluate the expression.

17. $4\frac{1}{5} \cdot \left(3\frac{3}{7} - 1\frac{9}{14}\right)$

18. $\frac{5}{9} - \left(\frac{5}{6} - \frac{1}{3}\right)^2$

19. An outdoor hot tub needs $\frac{3}{4}$ ounce of algaecide every day to kill algae growth. You buy a 30 ounce bottle of algaecide. How many days of use will you get from the bottle?

Answers

1. _____
2. _____
3. _____
4. _____
5. _____
6. _____
7. _____
8. _____
9. _____
10. _____
11. _____
12. _____
13. _____
14. _____
15. _____
16. _____
17. _____
18. _____
19. _____

Name _____ Date _____

Chapter Test C
For use after Chapter 5

Write the fraction or mixed number as a decimal.

20. $\dfrac{9}{11}$ **21.** $3\dfrac{7}{15}$ **22.** $\dfrac{3}{32}$

Answers

20. _____

21. _____

In Exercises 23–25, write the decimal as a fraction or mixed number.

23. -2.64 **24.** 0.052 **25.** $0.\overline{03}$

22. _____

23. _____

26. The table shows the fraction of people in a survey that named each type of music as their favorite. Order the types of music from most popular to least popular.

24. _____

25. _____

Type of music	Rock	Pop	Jazz	Country	Classical
Fraction of people	$\dfrac{5}{12}$	$\dfrac{2}{9}$	$\dfrac{1}{20}$	$\dfrac{4}{15}$	$\dfrac{1}{32}$

26. _____

27. _____

Find the sum, difference, product or quotient.

28. _____

27. $16.4 - (-9.73)$ **28.** $-0.876 + (-0.08)$

29. $4.03 (0.116)$ **30.** $5.814 \div 1.53$

29. _____

30. _____

In Exercises 31 and 32, evaluate the expression.

31. $2.4^2 + 3.08 \div 0.4 \cdot 1.2$ **32.** $(6.7 + 4.64) \div 4.5^2$

31. _____

32. _____

33. Use front-end estimation to estimate the sum:
$8.23 + 6.11 + 9.75 + 3.95$.

33. _____

34. You are looking at two area rugs for your bedroom. One is a square with a side length of 6.3 feet. The other is a rectangle that is 4.8 feet by 8.2 feet. Which rug will cover the greater area? How much more area will it cover?

34. _____

_____

35. You need a 93 point average to receive an A in a science class. The point scores on your tests so far are 90, 96, 89, and 93. What score do you need on your last test to have a 93 point average? If you get that score, what will the median and range of your test scores be?

35. _____

_____

Name _____ Date _____

Standardized Test

For use after Chapter 5

1. You walk $6\frac{2}{3}$ miles of a $10\frac{1}{3}$ mile trek. How much farther do you have to walk?

Ⓐ $3\frac{2}{3}$ miles Ⓑ $3\frac{1}{3}$ miles

Ⓒ $4\frac{2}{3}$ miles Ⓓ $4\frac{1}{3}$ miles

2. What is the sum $\frac{5}{8} + \frac{7}{12} + \frac{1}{6}$?

Ⓕ $1\frac{1}{4}$ Ⓖ $\frac{21}{24}$ Ⓗ $1\frac{3}{8}$ Ⓘ $1\frac{1}{12}$

3. Your uncle is cementing a patio. The patio is $10\frac{3}{5}$ feet long and $8\frac{3}{4}$ feet wide. What is the area of the patio?

Ⓐ $38\frac{7}{8}$ ft^2 Ⓑ $19\frac{7}{20}$ ft^2

Ⓒ $46\frac{3}{8}$ ft^2 Ⓓ $92\frac{3}{4}$ ft^2

4. What is the quotient $-\frac{5}{8} \div \frac{10}{13}$?

Ⓕ $-1\frac{12}{13}$ Ⓖ $-\frac{13}{16}$ Ⓗ $-\frac{13}{32}$ Ⓘ $-1\frac{6}{13}$

5. Solve $-\frac{7}{12}a = \frac{5}{8}$.

Ⓐ $1\frac{1}{14}$ Ⓑ $\frac{14}{15}$ Ⓒ $-1\frac{1}{14}$ Ⓓ $-\frac{14}{15}$

6. At a baseball game, $\frac{11}{36}$ of the fans bought hot dogs. What is another way to express this number?

Ⓕ $0.30\overline{5}$ Ⓖ 0.31

Ⓗ $0.\overline{305}$ Ⓘ $0.3\overline{05}$

7. What is the difference $3.08 - 2.165$?

Ⓐ 0.843 Ⓑ 1.085

Ⓒ 0.925 Ⓓ 0.915

8. For 3 days, rain accumulations were 1.36 inches, 2.05 inches, and 1.7 inches. What was the rain total by the end of the third day?

Ⓕ 4.48 inches Ⓖ 5.11 inches

Ⓗ 5.56 inches Ⓘ 3.58 inches

9. Solve $2.36x = 2.95$.

Ⓐ 0.8 Ⓑ 0.59

Ⓒ 1.25 Ⓓ 6.962

10. Which fraction is greater than 0.58?

Ⓕ $\frac{14}{25}$ Ⓖ $\frac{7}{12}$ Ⓗ $\frac{11}{20}$ Ⓘ $\frac{4}{7}$

Short Response

11. Water is coming out of a sprinkler at a rate of 8 gallons in 5 minutes. How much water is coming out each minute? How much water will come out in 17 minutes? Show your work.

Extended Response

12. The data set shows the weights, in grams, of several snakes. Find the mean, median, mode(s), and range of the data set 56, 61, 81, 55, 61, 58, 55, 60, 53. Which is most representative of the weights of the snakes? Explain your reasoning.

Name _____ Date _____

Alternative Assessment and Math Journal

For use after Chapter 5

Journal 1. In this chapter you learned how to work with fractions. In your own words explain how you add, subtract, multiply, and divide fractions. Be sure to indicate which of the operations require a common denominator.

Multi-Step Problem 2. Becky and Juan are cleaning swimming pools to earn money for the summer. They charge each customer a set price for pool cleaning, based on how long they originally estimated the job to take. They currently have eight customers. The actual times it takes to clean their customers' pools are shown in the table:

Customer number	1	2	3	4	5	6	7	8
Cleaning time (hours)	$2\frac{1}{4}$	$3\frac{1}{8}$	$1\frac{3}{4}$	$1\frac{3}{8}$	$1\frac{3}{4}$	$2\frac{1}{8}$	$2\frac{1}{4}$	$1\frac{3}{4}$

a. Order the numbers for the cleaning times from least to greatest.

b. Find the difference between the pool that takes them the greatest amount of time to clean and the pool that takes them the least amount of time to clean.

c. Convert the numbers from part (a) to decimals.

d. For the eight customers, what is the mean amount of time it takes Juan and Becky to clean a pool?

e. What is the median amount of time it takes Juan and Becky to clean a pool?

f. What is the mode of the times it takes for them to clean a pool?

g. One of the customers whose pool takes $1\frac{3}{4}$ hours to clean has a friend whose pool should take twice as long to clean. How much time should Becky and Juan schedule to clean the friend's pool?

h. The Baker family is charged $14.56 for pool cleaning and it takes $1\frac{3}{4}$ hours. The Jones family is charged $17.34 for pool cleaning and it takes $2\frac{1}{8}$ hours. Which family is getting the better hourly rate?

Name _____ Date _____

Alternative Assessment Rubric

For use after Chapter 5

Journal Solution

1. Complete answers should include:

• To multiply or divide fractions, there is no restriction on having a common denominator. To multiply two fractions, you simply put the product of the numerators over the product of the denominators. Division of two fractions can be rewritten as multiplication, after you invert the second fraction.

• To add or subtract two fractions, you must first get a common denominator. Then you add or subtract the numerators and write the sum or difference over the common denominator.

Multi-Step Problem Solution

2. a. $1\frac{3}{8}$, $1\frac{3}{4}$, $1\frac{3}{4}$, $1\frac{3}{4}$, $2\frac{1}{8}$, $2\frac{1}{4}$, $2\frac{1}{4}$, $3\frac{1}{8}$

b. $1\frac{3}{4}$ h

c. In order from least to greatest: 1.375, 1.75, 1.75, 1.75, 2.125, 2.25, 2.25, 3.125

d. 2.047 h

e. 1.9375 h

f. 1.75 h

g. 3.5 h

h. The Jones family is paying $.16 less per hour.

Multi-Step Problem Rubric

4 The student correctly computes each answer and uses the correct representations.

3 The student misses one or two of the parts but has no trouble converting the fractions into decimals.

2 The student misses three or four of the parts and/or the student has trouble converting the fractions into decimals.

1 The student misses more than four parts and/or the work is sloppy and illogical.

Name _____ Date _____

Quiz 1

For use after Lessons 6.1–6.3

In Exercises 1–6, solve the equation.

1. $7(y - 6) = 28$

2. $-99 = 12(z - 3) + 6z$

3. $15a - 56 = 13a$

4. $48 - 9x = -27 + 6x$

5. $17.6n - 18.28 = 21.8n - 41.8$

6. $-\dfrac{1}{6}m - \dfrac{5}{8} + \dfrac{3}{4}m = 1\dfrac{3}{4}$

7. The sides of the triangle are equal in length. Find the perimeter of the triangle.

$(3x + 11)$ m

$(5x - 6)$ m

8. A movie ticket for an adult costs \$6.95 and a movie ticket for a child costs \$4.25. A family with an equal number of adults and children goes to a movie and spends \$40.35. If the total also included \$6.75 for popcorn, how many adults and children went to the movie?

Answers

1. _____

2. _____

3. _____

4. _____

5. _____

6. _____

7. _____

8. _____

McDougal Littell Math, Course 3
Chapter 6   Assessment Book

Name _____ Date _____

6 Quiz 2

For use after Lessons 6.4–6.6

Complete the statement, where *r* = radius, *d* = diameter, and *C* = circumference. Use 3.14 or $\frac{22}{7}$ for π.

Answers

1. $d =$ ____, $C = 88$ cm

2. $C = 56.52$ in., $r =$ ____

Solve the inequality.

3. $5x - 11 < 19$

4. $-7x - 8 \geq 2x + 19$

5. $-4(y - 6) > -7y$

6. $1.23 \leq -3.6y - 14.31 + 7.3y$

In Exercises 7 and 8, translate the verbal phrase into an inequality. Then solve the inequality.

7. Nine times a number minus 6 is at least 66.

8. Three times the sum of a number and 7 is at most 15.

9. An athlete wants to consume at least 2525 calories a day while he is in training. So far today he has consumed 1725 calories. The spaghetti and sauce he is eating for dinner has about 320 calories per cup. How many cups should he eat to meet his minimum calorie requirements?

1. _____
2. _____
3. _____
4. _____
5. _____
6. _____
7. _____
8. _____
9. _____

CHAPTER 6 Chapter Test A

For use after Chapter 6

Identify the like terms in the expression.

1. $3m - 7 - 11m + 5n$

2. $15 - x + 6y - 2$

Solve the equation.

3. $9a - 7a - 5 = -11$

4. $\dfrac{b + 8}{3} = 7$

5. $6w = -8w + 70$

6. $4(c + 3) = 2c$

In Exercises 7–10, tell what number you would multiply each side of the equation by to eliminate the decimals or fractions. Then solve the equation.

7. $2.12 = 1.2m + 0.32$

8. $\dfrac{3}{5}q - 1\dfrac{2}{5} = 2q$

9. $22 = \dfrac{1}{4}x + \dfrac{2}{3}x$

10. $3.5g - 6.3 = 2.1g + 4.2$

11. Mark wants to save \$380 for a new digital camera. He has saved \$120 and earns \$6.25 an hour working at a grocery store. Use the verbal model to write an equation to find the number of hours Mark needs to work to have enough money to purchase the camera.

$$\boxed{\begin{array}{c}\text{Dollars}\\\text{saved}\end{array}} + \left(\boxed{\begin{array}{c}\text{Hourly}\\\text{wage}\end{array}} \cdot \boxed{\begin{array}{c}\text{Hours}\\\text{worked}\end{array}}\right) = \boxed{\begin{array}{c}\text{Total}\\\text{savings}\end{array}}$$

12. Solve the equation you wrote in Exercise 11.

13. The sides of the triangle are equal in length and are measured in feet. Find the perimeter of the triangle.

$5x + 8$

$7x$

Answers

1. _____
2. _____
3. _____
4. _____
5. _____
6. _____
7. _____
8. _____
_____
9. _____
_____
10. _____
_____
11. _____
12. _____
13. _____

Name _____ Date _____

Chapter Test A

For use after Chapter 6

Complete the statement, where r = radius, d = diameter, and C = circumference. Use 3.14 or $\frac{22}{7}$ for π.

14. $r =$ _____, $d = 15$ in.

15. $d = 14$ m, $C =$ _____

16. $r = 8$ cm, $C =$ _____

17. $d =$ _____, $C = 110$ ft

Solve the inequality. Then graph its solution.

18. $3x - 2 \leq 7$

<----+---+---+---+---+---+---+---+---+---+---->

19. $5y - 8 + 2y > 6$

<----+---+---+---+---+---+---+---+---+---+---->

20. $9m - 7 < 4m + 8$

<----+---+---+---+---+---+---+---+---+---+---->

21. $3 > 2(z - 3)$

<----+---+---+---+---+---+---+---+---+---+---->

Translate the verbal phrase into an inequality. Let x represent the unknown number.

22. A number plus 7 is at most 21.

23. Twice a number is less than 15.

In Exercises 24–26, use the following information. You have $75 to spend at a sporting goods store. You pick out a fishing rod for $52. Fishing lures are $4.75 each. At most how many fishing lures can you buy with the new fishing rod?

24. Write a variable expression for the total cost of your purchase.

25. Use the expression from Exercise 24 to write an inequality for the number of lures you can buy.

26. Solve the inequality. Explain what the solution means in this case.

Answers

14. _____

15. _____

16. _____

17. _____

18. _____

___See left.___

19. _____

___See left.___

20. _____

___See left.___

21. _____

___See left.___

22. _____

23. _____

24. _____

25. _____

26. _____

_____

_____

_____

_____

Chapter Test B

For use after Chapter 6

In Exercises 1–8, solve the equation.

1. $9z - 13 + 3z = 11$

2. $-10 = -5(3m - 7)$

3. $15 - 3x = 27 - 7x$

4. $3(x + 7) = 7x - 15$

5. $0.78p = 1.2p - 2.52$

6. $\frac{3}{5}\left(\frac{2}{3}x - \frac{5}{6}\right) = 3$

7. $\frac{5q - 11}{3} = \frac{7}{9}$

8. $0.5w - 1.32 + 1.2w = 0.4w + 8.04$

9. The sides of the triangle are equal in length and are measured in inches. Find the perimeter of the triangle.

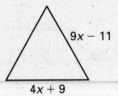

$9x - 11$

$4x + 9$

10. A local library is keeping track of book circulation. The number of books borrowed this year is 136 more than twice the number of books borrowed last year. The library loaned out 5472 books this year. How many books did it loan out last year?

11. You and a friend go shopping for food for a picnic. You spend $7.25 on hot dogs and buy 5 packages of buns. Your friend spends $9.15 on ground meat for hamburgers and buys 3 packages of buns. Hot dog and hamburger buns cost the same per package. You both spend the same amount of money. How much is a package of buns?

Answers

1. _____

2. _____

3. _____

4. _____

5. _____

6. _____

7. _____

8. _____

9. _____

10. _____

11. _____

Name _____ Date _____

Chapter Test B

For use after Chapter 6

In Exercises 12 and 13, complete the statement, where r = radius, d = diameter, and C = circumference. Use 3.14 or $\frac{22}{7}$ for π.

12. $r =$ ____, $C = 15.7$ m   **13.** $d = 24$ in., $C =$ ____

14. A rotating sprinkler is shooting water a distance of 15 feet. What is the circumference of the circle of lawn being watered by the sprinkler?

Solve the inequality. Then graph its solution.

15. $6a + 11 > -7$

‹––+––+––+––+––+––+––+––+––+––+––›

16. $44 \leq 17 - 3b$

‹––+––+––+––+––+––+––+––+––+––+––›

17. $26 > 4c + 15 + 8c$

‹––+––+––+––+––+––+––+––+––+––+––›

18. $-6(d - 11) \geq 30$

‹––+––+––+––+––+––+––+––+––+––+––›

19. $\frac{1}{2}e + \frac{2}{3} \leq \frac{2}{3}e + \frac{1}{2}$

‹––+––+––+––+––+––+––+––+––+––+––›

20. $0.3(0.2f - 1.1) < 3.804$

‹––+––+––+––+––+––+––+––+––+––+––›

In Exercises 21 and 22, translate the verbal phrase into an inequality. Then solve the inequality.

21. 7 times the difference of 8 and a number is more than 28.

22. 6 less than the product of 3 and a number is no more than 15.

23. You have $150 in a savings account and earn $6.50 an hour babysitting. Your brother has $275 in a savings account and earns $5 an hour delivering newspapers. You both work the same number of hours. At least how many hours do you need to work to have more money than your brother?

Answers

12. _____

13. _____

14. _____

15. _____

_____See left._____

16. _____

_____See left._____

17. _____

_____See left._____

18. _____

_____See left._____

19. _____

_____See left._____

20. _____

_____See left._____

21. _____

_____

22. _____

_____

23. _____

Name _____ Date _____

Chapter Test C

For use after Chapter 6

In Exercises 1–6, solve the equation.

1. $13x + 7x - 4x = -40$

2. $\dfrac{y - 8}{5} = \dfrac{y + 3}{2}$

3. $5z - 3(6 - z) = 54$

4. $7p - 5 + 2p = 3p + 13$

5. $\dfrac{2}{3}\left(\dfrac{3}{4}m - \dfrac{1}{6}\right) = m + \dfrac{1}{3}$

6. $0.7(0.3q - 1.1) = 1.1q + 0.832$

7. The area of the triangle is 66 square units. Write an equation for the area of the triangle. Then solve for x.

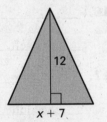

12

$x + 7$

8. Lori has a cell phone that costs $17.25 a month plus $.15 a minute for any long distance calls. Maryann has a cell phone that costs $12.35 a month plus $.25 a minute for any long distance calls. Their phone bills were equal this month, and they both used the same amount of long distance minutes. How many minutes of long distance did they each use?

9. The sides of the triangle are equal in length and are measured in millimeters. Find the perimeter of the triangle.

$5(2x - 6)$ $3(x + 4)$

10. At a pet store, you buy a bird feeder for $35. You also buy $13\dfrac{1}{3}$ pounds of sunflower seeds and $4\dfrac{1}{2}$ pounds of thistle seed. Thistle seed is twice the price of sunflower seeds. Your bill comes to $68.50. How much was the sunflower seed per pound?

1. _____

2. _____

3. _____

4. _____

5. _____

6. _____

7. _____

8. _____

9. _____

10. _____

Name _____ Date _____

Chapter Test C

For use after Chapter 6

In Exercises 11 and 12, complete the statement, where _r_ = radius,
_d_ = diameter, and _C_ = circumference. Use 3.14 or $\frac{22}{7}$ for π.

11. $r =$ ____, $C = 66$ ft   **12.** $d = 5\frac{3}{4}$ mm, $C =$ ____

13. A company is making cans with a $1\frac{1}{2}$ inch radius. A piece of metal
wraps around the circular top and bottom to form the outside of the
can. The piece overlaps itself at the seam by $\frac{1}{8}$ inch. How long is this
piece of metal? Use $\frac{22}{7}$ for π.

14. The circumference of the outer concentric
circle is 50.24 inches. Find x. Use 3.14 for π.

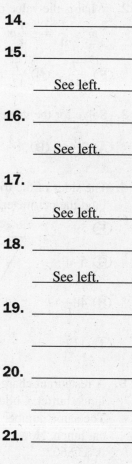

Solve the inequality. Then graph the solution.

15. $5e + 7 - 18e \le 46$

<++++++++++++++++++>

16. $0.35 - 0.7k > 1.26$

<++++++++++++++++++>

17. $\frac{2}{3}m - \frac{5}{6} < \frac{1}{3}m$

<++++++++++++++++++>

18. $\frac{1}{5}\left(p - \frac{1}{3}\right) \ge \frac{2}{3}p - 1$

<++++++++++++++++++>

In Exercises 19–21, translate the verbal phrase into an inequality.
Then solve the inequality.

19. 8 times the difference of 15 and a number is no less than 70.

20. The sum of a number and 9 is more than 3 times the difference of
4 and the number.

21. 15 less than 4 times a number is, at most, 11 more than twice
the number.

22. A health club offers exercise classes for $35 a term for nonmembers. If
you join the club for $72 a year, the classes are only $18 a term. How
many terms do you have to take classes so that being a member costs
less than paying the nonmember fees?

Answers

11. _____

12. _____

13. _____

14. _____

15. _____

See left.

16. _____

See left.

17. _____

See left.

18. _____

See left.

19. _____

20. _____

_____

21. _____

_____

22. _____

Multiple Choice

1. What is the value of x in the equation
$5x - 6 = 2x + 18$?

  (A) 4   (B) 8   (C) -4 (D) -8

2. What is the value of m in the equation
$\frac{2}{3}m - \frac{1}{4} = -\frac{1}{4}m + \frac{1}{3}$?

  (F) $\frac{77}{144}$ (G) $\frac{7}{12}$ (H) $\frac{7}{11}$ (I) $\frac{11}{12}$

3. Solve for the value of y: $35 = 8(y - 3)$.

  (A) $7\frac{3}{8}$ (B) $4\frac{3}{4}$ (C) 4 (D) $1\frac{3}{8}$

4. The sides of the triangle are equal in length.
Find the perimeter of the triangle.

  (F) 59

  (G) 5

  (H) $48\frac{3}{17}$

  (I) 117

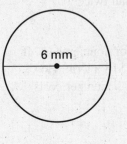

$5x + 14$

$3(4x - 7)$

5. A restaurant charges adults \$5.95 for its
lunch buffet. Children are charged \$2.95.
The same number of children and adults
eat lunch. How many adults eat if the bill
is \$35.60?

  (A) 3   (B) 4   (C) 5   (D) 6

6. Find the circumference of the circle.
Use 3.14 for π.

  (F) 18.84 mm

  (G) 9.42 mm

  (H) 37.68 mm

  (I) 113.04 mm

6 mm

7. A coffee mug has a circumference of
15.7 inches. What is the radius of the mug?

  (A) 5 in.   (B) $2\frac{1}{4}$ in.

  (C) $3\frac{1}{2}$ in.   (D) $2\frac{1}{2}$ in.

8. What is the value of x in the inequality
$6x - 11 \le -17$?

  (F) $x \le -1$ (G) $x \le -4\frac{2}{3}$

  (H) $x \ge -1$ (I) $x \ge -4\frac{2}{3}$

9. Which inequality represents the verbal
phrase "14 times the difference of 8 and a
number is at least 26"?

  (A) $14(8 - n) > 26$ (B) $14(8 - n) < 26$

  (C) $14(8 - n) \ge 26$ (D) $14(8 - n) \le 26$

Short Response

10. The sum of 4 consecutive even integers is
108. Write an equation to find the integers.
Then list the integers.

Extended Response

11. You have \$370. You find a DVD player that
costs \$257. New release movies cost \$21
and older release movies cost \$14. Write
and solve an inequality to find the number
of movies you can buy for your new DVD
player if you buy an equal number of old
and new movies.

CHAPTER 6 Alternative Assessment and Math Journal

For use after Chapter 6

Journal

1. In this chapter you learned how to solve inequalities and equations involving fractions and decimals. Solve the following inequality:
$$\frac{3}{5}x - \frac{2}{7}x + 1\frac{3}{5} \geq 0.12x + 9 - 0.07x.$$
In your own words explain how you performed each step of the solution.

Multi-Step Problem

2. You work for a company that designs tin cans. One of your products is a standard size soup can with dimensions as given in the figure.

$r = 1\frac{1}{2}$ in.

$h = 4\frac{3}{8}$ in.

a. Find the diameter of the top of the soup can.

b. Find the circumference of the top of the soup can.

c. A larger soup can has a top with a radius that is double the radius of the soup can shown in the figure. Find the circumference of the larger can.

d. You are asked to design a soup can with the same height as the can shown in the figure. However, this soup can is supposed to have a circumference that is equal to the height of the can. Write an equation to find the radius of this new can.

e. Solve the equation from part (d) to find the radius of the can you designed. Round your answer to four decimal places.

f. The radius of a paint can is determined by the following equation:
$2\pi(r - 3) = \pi(r - 1)$.
Solve the equation to find the radius of the paint can.

g. You want to design a can with a top that has a circumference from 9 inches to 11 inches. Write a compound inequality to represent this statement in terms of π and r.

h. Solve your inequality from part (g) to find a range of values that r can assume. Use 3.14 for π. Round your answer to the nearest hundredth.

Name _____ Date _____

Alternative Assessment Rubric

For use after Chapter 6

Journal Solution

1. $x \geq 28$; Complete answers should include the following:

- To clear fractions from an equation or inequality, you can multiply each side of the equation or inequality by the LCD.

- To clear decimals from an equation or inequality, you can multiply each side of the equation or inequality by 100.

- Combine like terms.

- Perform mathematical operations.

Multi-Step Problem Solution

2. a. 3 in.

b. 9.42 in.

c. 18.84 in.

d. $2\pi r = 4.375$

e. $r \approx 0.6966$ in.

f. 5 units

g. $9 \leq 2\pi r \leq 11$

h. 1.43 in. $\leq r \leq 1.75$ in.

Multi-Step Problem Rubric

4 The student correctly answers each question, including appropriate units where needed and appropriate notation for inequalities.

3 The student answers each question but either answers one question incorrectly or does not include appropriate units or appropriate notation where needed.

2 The student answers each question but misses two or three parts of the problem.

1 The student does not answer all of the questions. The work is sloppy and/or incorrect.

Name _____ Date _____

Quiz 1

For use after Lessons 7.1–7.4

In Exercises 1 and 2, use the following information. A wooded acre lot has 12 oak trees, 8 maple trees, 5 hemlock trees, 6 cherry trees, and 10 beech trees. Write the ratio as a fraction in simplest form and in two other ways.

1. oak to cherry   **2.** beech to maple

3. A car traveled 320 miles on 10 gallons of gasoline. Write the unit rate for the miles per gallon.

Solve the proportion.

4. $\dfrac{a}{16} = \dfrac{25}{40}$ **5.** $\dfrac{12}{14} = \dfrac{42}{b}$ **6.** $\dfrac{9}{c} = \dfrac{21}{35}$

In Exercises 7–9, solve using a percent proportion.

7. 11 is what percent of 55?

8. What number is 42% of 125?

9. 15 is 25% of what number?

Write the decimal or fraction as a percent.

10. $\dfrac{30}{80}$ **11.** 0.025   **12.** 0.968

Complete the statement using <, >, or =.

13. $\dfrac{8}{25}$ ___ 3.2%   **14.** $\dfrac{2}{5}$ ___ 40%

Answers

1. _____

   _____

2. _____

   _____

   _____

3. _____

4. _____

5. _____

6. _____

7. _____

8. _____

9. _____

10. _____

11. _____

12. _____

13. _____

14. _____

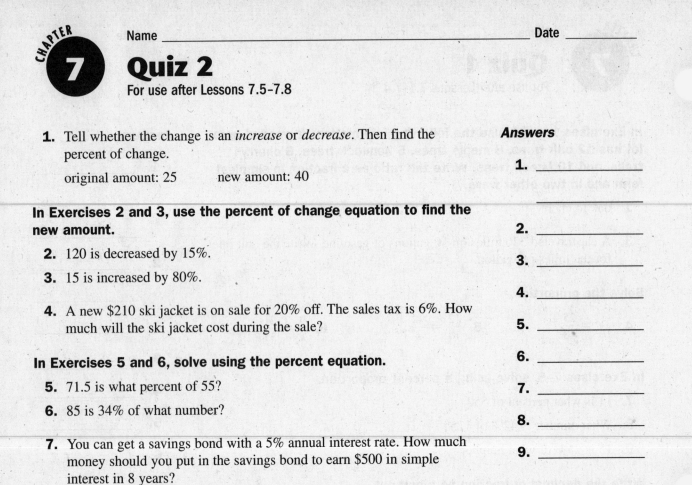

Quiz 2

For use after Lessons 7.5–7.8

1. Tell whether the change is an *increase* or *decrease*. Then find the percent of change.

original amount: 25   new amount: 40

In Exercises 2 and 3, use the percent of change equation to find the new amount.

2. 120 is decreased by 15%.

3. 15 is increased by 80%.

4. A new $210 ski jacket is on sale for 20% off. The sales tax is 6%. How much will the ski jacket cost during the sale?

In Exercises 5 and 6, solve using the percent equation.

5. 71.5 is what percent of 55?

6. 85 is 34% of what number?

7. You can get a savings bond with a 5% annual interest rate. How much money should you put in the savings bond to earn $500 in simple interest in 8 years?

In Exercises 8 and 9, use the following information.

You randomly draw a card from a bag that has the letters A through E printed on 75 cards. You do this 25 times, replacing the card each time. The results are summarized in the table.

Letter	A	B	C	D	E
Tally	4	5	9	4	3

8. Find the experimental probablity of drawing a card with a letter C.

9. Find the experimental probablity of *not* drawing a card with a letter B.

Answers

1. _____

_____

2. _____

3. _____

4. _____

5. _____

6. _____

7. _____

8. _____

9. _____

Name _____ Date _____

Chapter Test A

For use after Chapter 7

Write the ratio as a fraction in simplest form and in two other ways.

Answers

1. $\dfrac{8}{12}$

2. $\dfrac{35}{14}$

In Exercises 3 and 4, tell whether the ratios are equivalent.

3. 8 : 20 and 6 : 15

4. 9 to 15 and 21 to 28

5. A horse ran 11,000 feet in 5 minutes. Write the unit rate for the horse's speed.

Tell whether the ratios form a proportion.

6. $\dfrac{9}{15} \stackrel{?}{=} \dfrac{21}{35}$

7. $\dfrac{8}{14} \stackrel{?}{=} \dfrac{17}{28}$

In Exercises 8 and 9, solve the proportion.

8. $\dfrac{3}{5} = \dfrac{x}{20}$

9. $\dfrac{7}{y} = \dfrac{21}{27}$

10. A model car has a scale of 1 inch to 2 feet. The model car's length is 6 inches. Find the car's actual length.

Solve using a percent proportion.

11. 12 is what percent of 50?

12. 99 is 45% of what number?

13. What number is 30% of 70?

Write the decimal or fraction as a percent.

14. 0.03

15. $\dfrac{5}{4}$

16. $\dfrac{2}{5}$

1. _____

2. _____

3. _____

4. _____

5. _____

6. _____

7. _____

8. _____

9. _____

10. _____

11. _____

12. _____

13. _____

14. _____

15. _____

16. _____

Name _____ Date _____

Chapter Test A
For use after Chapter 7

Write the percent as a decimal and as a fraction.

17. 8%

18. 130%

Tell whether the change is an *increase* or *decrease*. Then find the percent of change.

19. 25 students to 32 students

20. 50 inches to 48 inches

Use the percent of change equation to find the new amount.

21. 80 is increased by 15%.

22. 220 is decreased by 37%.

In Exercises 23 and 24, find the sale price or retail price.

23. Original price: $125
Percent discount: 20%

24. Wholesale price: $12.75
Percent markup: 40%

25. A calculator costs $15.85. The sales tax is 6%. What is the total cost?

26. Find the amount of simple interest earned on $2500 at an annual interest rate of 3% for 6 years.

In Exercises 27 and 28, use the following information. The fruit drawer in your refrigerator contains 9 apples, 12 oranges, 6 peaches, and 9 pears. Find the probability of randomly choosing the fruit.

27. an apple

28. a peach

Answers

17. _____

18. _____

_____

19. _____

_____

20. _____

21. _____

22. _____

23. _____

24. _____

25. _____

26. _____

27. _____

28. _____

CHAPTER 7 Chapter Test B

For use after Chapter 7

Write the ratio as a fraction in simplest form and in two other ways.

1. 28 to 70

2. $-26 : 52$

In Exercises 3 and 4, write the equivalent rate.

3. $\dfrac{60 \text{ beats}}{1 \text{ min}} = \dfrac{? \text{ beats}}{1 \text{ h}}$

4. $\dfrac{\$5.64}{1} = \dfrac{?}{1 \text{ ft}}$

5. A store is advertising baby food for $3 for 5 jars. What is the unit price?

In Exercises 6–8, solve the proportion.

6. $\dfrac{21}{12} = \dfrac{d}{20}$

7. $\dfrac{e}{9} = \dfrac{91}{117}$

8. $\dfrac{18}{f} = \dfrac{15}{11}$

9. You can earn $26 babysitting 4 children. At this rate, what would you charge for 3 children?

10. A map uses a scale of 2 cm : 15 km. The distance from Hickory to Pleasantville is 17 centimeters on the map. How far apart are the two towns?

Solve using a percent proportion.

11. 36 is what percent of 240?

12. 726 is 110% of what number?

Write the percent as a decimal and as a fraction.

13. 6%

14. 310%

15. 0.5%

Write the decimal or fraction as a percent.

16. 0.025

17. $\dfrac{83}{80}$

Answers

1. _____

_____

_____

2. _____

_____

_____

3. _____

4. _____

5. _____

6. _____

7. _____

8. _____

9. _____

10. _____

11. _____

12. _____

13. _____

_____

14. _____

_____

15. _____

_____

16. _____

17. _____

In Exercises 18 and 19, use the percent of change equation to find the new amount.

Answers

18. 1570 is increased by 36%.

18. _____

19. 540 is decreased by 52.5%.

19. _____

20. A school band had 350 members last year. This year there are 329 members. What is the percent of change in members from last year to this year?

20. _____

21. A toy store buys video games at a wholesale price of $18.75. It marks up each game 60%. A customer has a coupon for 10% off a video game. How much will a video game cost with the coupon?

21. _____

22. You deposit $520 in a savings account. The account pays simple interest of 3.25%. How much interest will you earn in 3 years?

22. _____

23. _____

24. _____

In Exercises 23–25, find the probability of the event.

25. _____

23. Spinning a number greater than 5

26. _____

24. Spinning an even number

25. Not spinning a 3

26. In an experiment, 7 out of 15 results were positive outcomes. Predict how many positive outcomes will occur if the same experiment was repeated with a total of 60 results.

Name _____ Date _____

Chapter Test C

For use after Chapter 7

Write the rate as a unit rate.

1. A secretary typed 372 words in 6 minutes.

2. It costs $3 for a 10-pound bag of birdseed.

In Exercises 3–5, solve the proportion.

3. $\dfrac{38}{95} = \dfrac{x}{85}$

4. $\dfrac{15}{y} = \dfrac{21}{49}$

5. $\dfrac{z}{18} = \dfrac{32}{12}$

6. A town's election committee expects 5 out of every 7 registered voters to vote in the next election. The town has 21,000 registered voters. How many people are expected to vote?

In Exercises 7 and 8, find the value of x.

7. $\dfrac{16}{20} = \dfrac{24}{x+3}$

8. $\dfrac{x-6}{48} = \dfrac{34}{51}$

9. A builder is using a blueprint that has a scale of 2 inches to 5 feet. If a wall on the blueprint measures 5 inches, how long should the actual wall be?

In Exercises 10 and 11, solve using a percent proportion.

10. 132.5 is 125% of what number?

11. 14.7 is what percent of 42?

12. Order the numbers from least to greatest:
    0.4, $\dfrac{11}{32}$, 39%, $\dfrac{3}{8}$, 0.38.

Complete the statement using <, >, or =.

13. 0.35% __ $\dfrac{7}{200}$

14. 3.025 __ $3\dfrac{1}{400}$

Answers

1. _____

2. _____

3. _____

4. _____

5. _____

6. _____

7. _____

8. _____

9. _____

10. _____

11. _____

12. _____

13. _____

14. _____

In Exercises 15 and 16, find the percent of increase or decrease.

Answers

15. $2x$ to $5x$

16. $\frac{2}{3}x$ to $\frac{1}{6}x$

15. _____

16. _____

17. There were 24 bald eagles in a nature reserve last year. This year there are 31 eagles. What is the percent of change?

17. _____

18. A woman bought $13,752 worth of stock in 2000. By 2001, the value had decreased by 18%. That value then decreased by another 22% by the time she sold the stock. What was the value of the stock when she sold it?

18. _____

19. _____

19. The wholesale price of a winter coat is $45. The store marks up the coat 40%. At the end of the season, the coat is marked down 40%. Sales tax is 5%. What is the total price you pay for the coat at this time?

20. _____

21. _____

22. _____

20. How much money should you deposit in a savings account that pays 5% simple annual interest to earn $1200 in 8 years?

23. _____

In Exercises 21–23, use the following information. You get to a library just as it opens to watch the first 50 people enter the building. You record their hair color in the table. Find the probability.

21. The first person that leaves will have gray hair.

22. The first person to leave will not have brown hair.

23. Do Exercises 21 and 22 use theoretical probability or experimental probability?

Color	Tally
Black	11
Brown	17
Blonde	9
Red	6
Gray	7

Standardized Test

For use after Chapter 7

Multiple Choice

1. What is the ratio of shaded squares to unshaded squares?

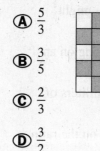

A $\frac{5}{3}$

B $\frac{3}{5}$

C $\frac{2}{3}$

D $\frac{3}{2}$

2. Which value of x makes the ratios $\frac{5}{8}$ and $\frac{x}{24}$ equivalent?

F 3   **G** 15   **H** 16   **I** 20

3. You earn $40 shoveling snow off 5 sidewalks. You charge the same amount for each sidewalk. How much will you earn if you shovel 3 sidewalks?

A $16   **B** $20   **C** $24   **D** $36

4. The scale on a drawing is 3 cm : 5 ft. A wood deck on the drawing measures 12 centimeters. How long is the actual deck?

F 15 feet   **G** 20 feet

H 25 feet   **I** 60 feet

5. What number is 65% of 74?

A 48.1   **B** 63.2   **C** 87.8   **D** 113.8

6. Which is equal to 0.025?

F 25%   **G** $\frac{1}{400}$ **H** $\frac{3}{120}$ **I** 0.25%

7. There were 150 blackbirds in a field on Monday. On Tuesday, there were 28% more. How many blackbirds were there in the field on Tuesday?

A 258   **B** 192   **C** 42   **D** 178

8. A savings account earns 4% annual interest. How much must you put into the account to earn $150 in 18 months?

F $900   **G** $208.33

H $5625   **I** $2500

9. You randomly pick a gumball from a container that has 26 red, 30 blue, 14 white, and 20 yellow gumballs. What is the probability of not getting a blue gumball?

A $\frac{1}{3}$ **B** $\frac{1}{2}$ **C** $\frac{2}{3}$ **D** $\frac{3}{4}$

Short Response

10. You buy a $55 computer game that is on sale for 20% off. Sales tax is 5%. Find the total price paid for the computer game. Explain how you found the answer.

Extended Response

11. A camping resort had 3120 camping sites rented in 2000. In 2001 they rented 2886 sites, and in 2002 they rented 3320 sites. Find the percent change from 2000 to 2001, from 2001 to 2002, and from 2000 to 2002. Round decimals to the nearest tenth, if necessary. Show your work.

CHAPTER 7 Alternative Assessment and Math Journal

For use after Chapter 7

Journal

1. In this chapter you learned about circle graphs. Explain what a circle graph is. What do you know about the sum of the fractions represented by the pieces of the circle graph? Give an example of a type of data you might use a circle graph to display.

Multi-Step Problem

2. Jamie works in a chemistry laboratory in her school. She is working on an experiment that yields a byproduct of hydrogen gas.

   a. For her experiment she needs 8 grams of zinc for every 5 milliliters of acid. Express this as a unit rate.

   b. If she starts with 12 grams of zinc, set up a proportion based on the ratio of zinc to acid in part (a).

   c. Solve the proportion you set up to find out how much acid is needed for 12 grams of zinc.

   d. Her experiment is expected to yield 175 milligrams of hydrogen gas. Due to the laboratory conditions, however, only 85% of the expected amount is produced. How much hydrogen gas is produced?

   e. The next time she conducted the experiment, 170 milligrams of hydrogen gas was produced. What is the percent increase from the amount you found in part (d)? Round your answer to the nearest tenth of a percent.

   f. In a different experiment, she obtained 76% of her expected yield. Express 76% as a fraction in lowest terms.

   g. Jamie's teacher randomly assigns her to work at one of the 16 lab stations in the chemistry laboratory. Three of these lab stations have broken lab equipment. What is the probability that Jamie gets assigned to one of the stations with broken equipment?

   h. Assume again that three of the lab stations have faulty equipment. Jamie is randomly assigned to work at a lab station each day for the next 47 days. Explain how you could approximate the number of days that Jamie would be placed at a station with faulty equipment.

Name _____ Date _____

Alternative Assessment Rubric

For use after Chapter 7

Journal Solution

1. Complete answers should include the following:

   • A circle graph represents data as parts of a circle. Each part is a percent of the data. The sum of the percents must equal 100% because the circle graph represents all of the data.

   • The sum of the fractions for each of the categories should be 1.

   • Examples will vary.

Multi-Step Problem Solution

2. a. 1.6 g per ml

   b. $\frac{8}{5} = \frac{12}{x}$, where x is the amount of acid in milliliters

   c. 7.5 ml

   d. 148.75 mg

   e. 14.3%

   f. $\frac{19}{25}$

   g. $\frac{3}{16}$

   h. Multiply the number of days Jamie works in the lab, 47, by the probability of her getting faulty equipment on any one day, $\frac{3}{16}$. Because $47 \times \frac{3}{16} \approx 8.8$, she probably will get faulty equipment on 8 or 9 days.

Multi-Step Problem Rubric

4 The student correctly answers each part and has a mathematically correct explanation for the writing exercise.

3 The student misses one or two parts. The writing exercise counts as two parts.

2 The student misses three or four parts. The writing exercise counts as two parts.

1 The student misses more than four parts of the problem.

McDougal Littell Math, Course 3
Chapter 7   Assessment Book

89

UNIT 2

Unit 2 Test
For use after Chapters 4–7

Write the prime factorization of the number.

1. 147   2. 112

Find the greatest common factor and the least common multiple.

3. 115, 20, 35   4. $18a^5b^4, 24a^3b^7$

Complete the statement with <, >, or =.

5. $\dfrac{45}{14}$ — $\dfrac{24}{7}$ 6. $1\dfrac{7}{15}$ — $\dfrac{11}{8}$

Multiply or divide. Write your answer as a power.

7. $9^7 \cdot 9^5$ 8. $\dfrac{17^{16}}{17^{11}}$

In Exercises 9 and 10, write the expression using only positive exponents.

9. $3^2x^6y^{-3} \cdot 3^5x^{-4}y^{-2}$ 10. $\dfrac{5^{-3}a^7}{5^{-5}a^{-4}}$

11. A commercial airplane flew 2,080,000 miles before being replaced with a new plane. Write this number in scientific notation.

In Exercises 12–17, find the sum, difference, product, or quotient.

12. $-\dfrac{7}{8} + \dfrac{3}{8}$ 13. $7\dfrac{2}{11} - 4\dfrac{6}{11}$ 14. $3\dfrac{2}{5} + 2\dfrac{4}{15}$

15. $\dfrac{4}{15} \cdot \dfrac{5}{12}$ 16. $4\dfrac{2}{3} \cdot 3\dfrac{4}{7}$ 17. $3\dfrac{3}{8} \div 6$

18. Today you ran a mile in $10\dfrac{3}{8}$ minutes. Yesterday it took you

$11\dfrac{5}{16}$ minutes. How much faster were you today?

Find the sum, difference, product, or quotient.

19. $17.18 - 12.749$ 20. $-0.062 + (-0.71)$

21. $4.875 \div 0.78$ 22. $0.0035 \cdot 0.142$

Answers

1. _____
2. _____
3. _____
4. _____
5. _____
6. _____
7. _____
8. _____
9. _____
10. _____
11. _____
12. _____
13. _____
14. _____
15. _____
16. _____
17. _____
18. _____
19. _____
20. _____
21. _____
22. _____

Name _____ Date _____

Unit 2 Test
For use after Chapters 4–7

Solve the equation.

23. $4.52 + x = 3.6$ **24.** $3(w - 4) = 18$

In Exercises 25–27, write the fraction as a decimal or write the decimal as a fraction.

25. $\frac{8}{15}$ **26.** 0.04 **27.** $0.\overline{36}$

28. Your mom bought a gallon of milk for $3.65, and 3 pounds of ham. Your grandmother bought 2 pounds of ham and a container of laundry detergent that cost $5.75. They both spent the same amount of money. How much did the ham cost per pound?

Find the indicated measurement, where r = radius, d = diameter, and C = circumference. Use 3.14 or $\frac{22}{7}$ for π.

29. $C = 94.2$ cm, $r =$ _____   **30.** $d = 35$ ft, $C =$ _____

In Exercises 31 and 32, solve the inequality.

31. $8k - 7 - 12k \le 9$ **32.** $12(s - 6) > 30$

33. A landscaper needs at least 5000 cubic feet of topsoil to complete a job. He already has 3600 cubic feet of soil at the site. How many truck loads of soil should he have delivered if each truck load holds 600 cubic feet of soil?

In Exercises 34 and 35, write the equivalent rate.

34. $\dfrac{120 \text{ beats}}{1 \text{ min}} = \dfrac{?}{1 \text{ h}}$ **35.** $\dfrac{6 \text{ servings}}{1 \text{ pint}} = \dfrac{?}{1 \text{ quart}}$

36. At a zoo, 56% or 168 of the animals are mammals. How many animals does the zoo have?

In Exercises 37 and 38, write the percent as a decimal and as a fraction.

37. 42%   **38.** 210%

39. One day, a grocery store made 25% of its profit selling produce, and 33% of its profit selling meat. The store made $230 in profit on its produce. How much did it make on its meat?

In Exercises 40 and 41, use the following information. A box contains the letters MISSISSIPPI. You draw one letter from the box. Find the probability of the event.

40. Drawing the letter S   **41.** Not drawing an I

Answers

23. _____
24. _____
25. _____
26. _____
27. _____
28. _____
29. _____
30. _____
31. _____
32. _____
33. _____
34. _____
35. _____
36. _____
37. _____
38. _____
39. _____
40. _____
41. _____

Name _____ Date _____

Cumulative Test
For use after Chapters 1–7

Evaluate the expression.

1. $15 + \dfrac{18}{24 - 15}$

2. $21 + 8 \cdot 3 + 6$

3. $6^2 - 3^3 + 14$

4. $9^2 - (5 + 3)^2$

In Exercises 5 and 6, evaluate the expression when $a = 12$ and $b = 15$.

5. $15a - 3b$

6. $\dfrac{b + 21}{a - 4}$

7. Find the perimeter and area of a rectangle with a length of 17 meters and a width of 8 meters.

8. Over a four week period, a park sets an attendance record with 17,251 visitors. During the first three weeks the numbers of visitors were 4672, 3258, and 4996. How many visitors were there during the fourth week?

9. Order the integers from least to greatest: $-11, 6, -15, -4, 9, -21, -17$.

In Exercises 10–12, find the sum or difference.

10. $-15 + (-19)$

11. $9 - 17$

12. $-15 + 13$

13. Your school is arranging a ski trip. The lift tickets cost \$35 each and the bus ride costs \$17 per person. Write an expression to find the total cost for x students. Then find the cost for 21 students to attend.

Simplify the expression when $a = -2$, $b = 8$, and $c = -4$.

14. $\dfrac{b}{a}$

15. $7c - 3a$

16. $\dfrac{b^2}{ac}$

17. Plot and connect the given points in the coordinate plane. Then find the perimeter of the figure formed.

$A(-2, 4), B(-2, -1),$
$C(5, -1), D(5, 4)$

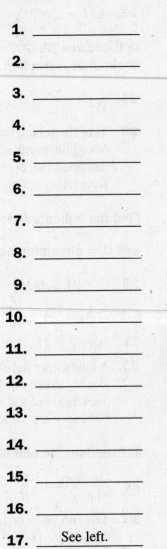

Answers

1. _____

2. _____

3. _____

4. _____

5. _____

6. _____

7. _____

8. _____

9. _____

10. _____

11. _____

12. _____

13. _____

14. _____

15. _____

16. _____

17. ____See left.____

Name _____ Date _____

Cumulative Test
For use after Chapters 1–7

In Exercises 18 and 19, solve the equation.

18. $x + 52 = -12$

19. $-17 = \dfrac{y}{6} - 14$

20. An ice-skating rink offers a birthday party special. There is a $75 rink charge and a $5.25 per person charge for food and skate rentals. One birthday party cost $185.25. Write and solve an equation to find the number of people that attended the party.

21. Find the area of the shaded region in the figure.

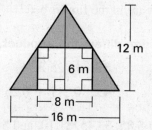

Solve the inequality. Then graph its solution.

22. $x + 15 < -6$

23. $\dfrac{2}{9} y \geq \dfrac{2}{3}$

Find the greatest common factor and least common multiple.

24. 84, 126

25. $21m^5 n^2$, $35mn^4$

In Exercises 26 and 27, write the fraction in simplest form.

26. $-\dfrac{45}{63}$

27. $\dfrac{21y}{14xy}$

28. A 50-pound bag of birdseed has 20 pounds of sunflower seeds in its mix. A 40-pound bag of birdseed has 15 pounds of sunflower seeds. Write fractions for the weight of sunflower seeds to the total weight in each bag. Which bag has the greater fraction of sunflower seeds?

In Exercises 29–31, multiply or divide. Write your answer using only positive exponents.

29. $m^{14} \cdot m^{-6}$

30. $\dfrac{8^3 x^{-4}}{8^{-5} x^2}$

31. $\dfrac{30a^5 b^7}{15a^9 b}$

32. Write the product in scientific notation: $\left(7 \times 10^{-5}\right) \times \left(3 \times 10^{-9}\right)$.

Answers

18. _____

19. _____

20. _____

21. _____

22. _____

_____See left._____

23. _____

_____See left._____

24. _____

_____

25. _____

_____

26. _____

27. _____

28. _____

29. _____

30. _____

31. _____

32. _____

Name _____ Date _____

Cumulative Test

For use after Chapters 1–7

In Exercises 33–36, solve the equation.

33. $a - \dfrac{5}{6} = \dfrac{7}{12}$

34. $b + \left(-1\dfrac{1}{5}\right) = -3\dfrac{8}{15}$

35. $\dfrac{3}{4}c = \dfrac{1}{2}$

36. $\dfrac{1}{2}d - 1\dfrac{3}{4} = 2\dfrac{7}{8}$

37. A gardener is planting a flower bed that is $3\dfrac{1}{2}$ feet wide by $10\dfrac{2}{3}$ feet long. How many square feet are in the flower bed?

In Exercises 38–41, find the sum, difference, product, or quotient.

38. $13.7 - 9.18$

39. $15.25(3.76)$

40. $34.136 \div 5.02$

41. $0.317 + 0.26$

42. Four items from a store cost \$.85, \$3.45, \$1.10, and \$4.46. Use front-end estimation to estimate how much money you will need to purchase the four items.

43. A bricklayer is building a brick sidewalk that is 3.5 feet wide by 31.25 feet long. How many square feet are in the sidewalk? How many bricks will be needed to build the sidewalk if each brick covers 0.125 square foot?

44. Find the mean, median, and mode(s) of the data set: 3, 6, 4, 7, 6, 2, 5, 4, 6.

In Exercises 45 and 46, solve the equation.

45. $2n - 5(n + 6) = 45$

46. $-45 - 11m = 24m + 25$

47. A chemical company has a cylindrical storage tank that has a diameter of 70 feet. The company wants to put up a security fence around the tank that is 20 feet away from the tank. How many feet of fence are needed?

Answers

33. _____

34. _____

35. _____

36. _____

37. _____

38. _____

39. _____

40. _____

41. _____

42. _____

43. _____

44. _____

_____

_____

45. _____

46. _____

47. _____

Cumulative Test
For use after Chapters 1–7

Translate the verbal phrase as an inequality. Let *n* represent the unknown number. Then solve the inequality.

48. 15 more than the product of 6 and a number is at least 27.

49. A number times 8 is less than the difference of twice the number and 21.

Write the rate as a unit rate.

50. $\dfrac{148 \text{ trees}}{4 \text{ acres}}$

51. $\dfrac{\$210}{40 \text{ hours}}$

Solve the proportion.

52. $\dfrac{15}{35} = \dfrac{x}{49}$

53. $\dfrac{16}{20} = \dfrac{36}{x}$

Solve using a percent proportion.

54. 70.2 is what percent of 260?

55. 76.2 is 127% of what number?

In Exercises 56 and 57, write the decimal or fraction as a percent.

56. 0.0125

57. $\dfrac{2}{25}$

58. A store buys a pair of boots wholesale for $25. The markup is 60%. At a weekend sale, the store offers the boots for 25% off the normal price. How much do the boots cost on sale?

Find the probability of the event.

59. You roll a number cube and get a number less than 3.

60. A randomly selected phone number will end with a 0 or 1.

Answers

48. _____

_____

49. _____

_____

50. _____

51. _____

52. _____

53. _____

54. _____

55. _____

56. _____

57. _____

58. _____

59. _____

60. _____

Name _____ Date _____

Quiz 1

For use after Lessons 8.1–8.4

Tell whether the angles are _complementary_, _supplementary_, or _neither_.

1. $m\angle 1 = 47°$, $m\angle 2 = 142°$

2. $m\angle 3 = 36°$, $m\angle 4 = 54°$

3. $\angle 5$ and $\angle 6$ are complementary, and $m\angle 5 = 28°$. Find $m\angle 6$.

Classify the triangle by its side lengths.

4. 5 m, 5 m, 5 m

5. 6 in., 8 in., 6 in.

6. 3 cm, 4 cm, 5 cm

Find the value of _x_.

7.

$(2x - 5)°$

$85°$

8.

$28°$

$95°$ $x°$

9.

$115°$ $115°$

$x°$ $105°$

$100°$

10. The angles of a quadrilateral measure 95°, 84°, 105°, and $x°$. Find the value of x.

Answers

1. _____
2. _____
3. _____
4. _____
5. _____
6. _____
7. _____
8. _____
9. _____
10. _____

8 Quiz 2

For use after Lessons 8.5–8.8

Explain how you know the triangles are congruent. Then write an equation and solve for x.

Answers

1.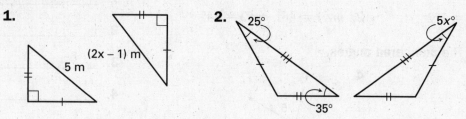

(2x – 1) m

5 m

2.   25°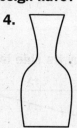

5x°

35°

How many lines of symmetry does the design have?

3.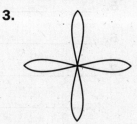

4.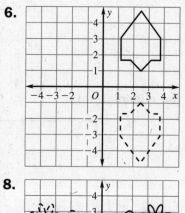

Name the type of transformation.

5.

6.

7.

8.

9. △ ABC is similar to △FGH.
Find the value of x.

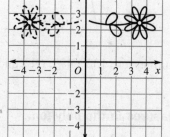

F   27.5 ft   H
12.5 ft   x
G

B
5 ft   8 ft
A
11 ft   C

Answers

1. _____

_____

2. _____

_____

3. _____

4. _____

5. _____

6. _____

7. _____

8. _____

9. _____

Chapter Test A

For use after Chapter 8

Tell whether the angles are *complementary*, *supplementary*, or *neither*.

1. $m\angle 1 = 58°$, $m\angle 2 = 122°$ **2.** $m\angle 1 = 46°$, $m\angle 2 = 44°$

Find the measures of the numbered angles.

3.

4.

In Exercises 5 and 6, classify the triangle by its side lengths.

5.

6.

7. Find the value of x. Then classify the triangle by its angles.

In Exercises 8 and 9, classify the quadrilateral.

8.

9.

10. The angles of a quadrilateral measure 132°, 47°, 69°, and $x°$. Find the value of x.

Find the sum of the angle measures in the polygon.

11. hexagon   **12.** 13-gon

Answers

1. _____

2. _____

3. _____

4. _____

_____

5. _____

6. _____

7. _____

_____

8. _____

9. _____

10. _____

11. _____

12. _____

In Exercces 13–16, use the following information. In the diagram, quadrilateral *GHIJ* quadrilateral *MNQP*.

13. Name four pairs of congruent angles.

14. Find $m\angle G$.

15. Find $m\angle Q$.

16. Find the length of $\overline{MP}$.

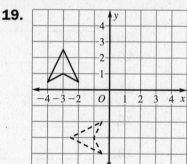

Answers

13. _____

_____

_____

_____

14. _____

15. _____

16. _____

17. _____

18. _____

19. _____

20. _____

21. _____

22. _____

Tell whether the images are reflections of each other.

17.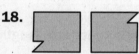

18.

In Exercises 19 and 20, name the type of transformation.

19.

20.

21. Name the similar polygons.

22. Logan is 6 feet tall and casts a 4 foot shadow. At the same time, Michael casts a 3 foot shadow. How tall is Michael?

Name _____ Date _____

Chapter Test B
For use after Chapter 8

Find the angle measure.

1. $\angle 1$ and $\angle 2$ are supplementary, and $m\angle 2 = 35°$. Find $m\angle 1$.

2. $\angle 3$ and $\angle 4$ are complementary, and $m\angle 3 = 40°$. Find $m\angle 4$.

In Exercises 3–6, use the diagram.

3. Find $m\angle 1$.

4. Find $m\angle 2$.

5. Find $m\angle 3$.

6. Which angle is supplementary to the 42° angle?

In Exercises 7 and 8, classify the triangle by its side lengths.

7.

8.

9. The angles of a triangle measure 35°, 73°, and $x°$. Find the value of x. Then classify the triangle by its angles.

In Exercises 10 and 11, classify the polygon.

10.

11.

12. A polygon with 6 sides is a _____.

Find the value of x.

13.

14.

In Exercises 15–18, quadrilateral $QRST \cong$ quadrilateral $KLMN$. Find the given measures.

15. $m\angle M$

16. $m\angle Q$

17. length of $\overline{MN}$

18. length of $\overline{KN}$

Answers

1. _____
2. _____
3. _____
4. _____
5. _____
6. _____
7. _____
8. _____
9. _____
   _____
10. _____
11. _____
12. _____
13. _____
14. _____
15. _____
16. _____
17. _____
18. _____

Name _____ Date _____

Chapter Test B

For use after Chapter 8

19. Graph the polygon $A(2, 1)$, $B(4, -1)$, $C(3, -3)$, and $D(1, -1)$. Then graph its reflection in the y-axis.

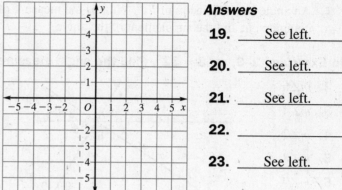

Answers

19. _____See left._____

20. _____See left._____

21. _____See left._____

22. _____

23. _____See left._____

In Exercises 20 and 21, graph the image of the transformation described.

20. Rotation 90° clockwise

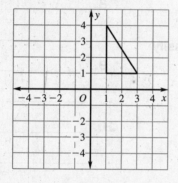

21. Translation using $(x, y) \rightarrow (x - 4, y + 2)$

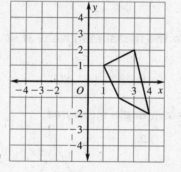

22. A 3-foot tall fence post casts a shadow 8 feet long. A silo next to the post casts a shadow 180 feet long. How tall is the silo?

23. Triangle EFG has vertices $E(2, 1)$, $F(4, 3)$, and $G(4, 1)$. Graph $\triangle EFG$ and its image after it is dilated by the scale factor $k = 3$.

Answers

1. An angle has a measure of 57°. What is the measure of the complement and the supplement of the angle?

1. _____

In Exercises 2–6, $m\angle 3 = 32°$. Find the angle measure.

2. _____

2. $m\angle 6$

3. _____

3. $m\angle 4$

4. $m\angle 2$

4. _____

5. $m\angle 8$

5. _____

6. $m\angle 9$

6. _____

7. _____

7. Find the value of x and the unknown angle measures.

8. _____

Can the angles in a triangle have the measures given? If so, classify the triangle by its angles.

9. _____

8. $30°, 45°, 105°$

9. $35°, 65°, 80°$

Find the value of x and the unknown angle measures.

10. _____

10.

11.

11. _____

12.

13.

12. _____

13. _____

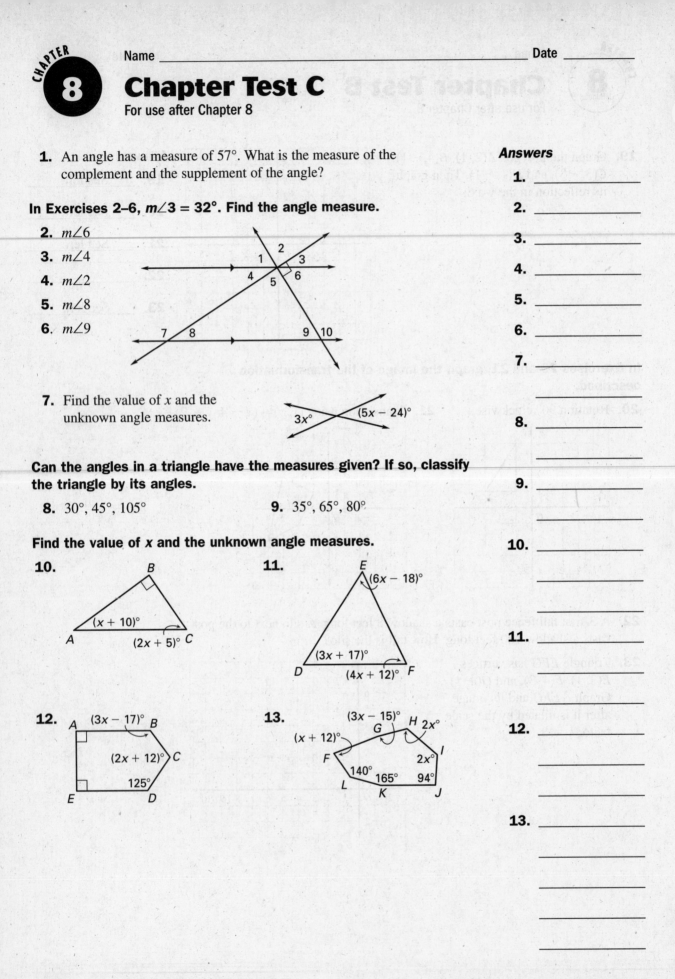

Name _____ Date _____

Chapter Test C

For use after Chapter 8

In Exercises 14 and 15, explain how you know the triangles are congruent. Then write an equation and solve for *x*.

14.

$(3x + 12)°$

$(4x - 11)°$

15. 15 m

$(7x - 6)$ m

16. Reflect $\triangle ABC$ in the *x*-axis to form $\triangle DEF$. Then reflect $\triangle DEF$ in the *y*-axis to form $\triangle HIJ$. Graph $\triangle HIJ$ on the coordinate grid and give the coordinates of the vertices.

17. Quadrilateral *RSTU* has vertices $R(3, 4)$, $S(6, 1)$, $T(5, -3)$, and $U(2, -4)$. Find the vertices of its image after the translation: $(x, y) \rightarrow (x - 6, y + 4)$.

18. Write the coordinates of the vertices of the image of $\triangle ABC$ after a 90° counterclockwise rotation. The coordinates of $\triangle ABC$ are $A(3, -4)$, $B(2, 0)$, and $C(2, 5)$.

19. A 4.5-foot tall mailbox is casting a shadow 8 feet long. A person standing next to the mailbox casts a 10-foot shadow. How tall is the person?

20. Triangle *ABC* has vertices $A(-3, 0)$, $B(-9, -3)$, and $C(-6, 3)$. Graph $\triangle ABC$ and its image after it is dilated by the scale factor of $k = \frac{1}{3}$.

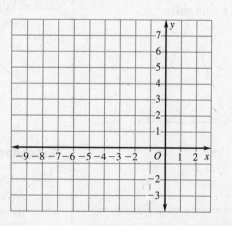

Answers

14. _____

_____

15. _____

_____

16. ___See left.___

_____

17. _____

_____

_____

_____

18. _____

_____

_____

19. _____

20. ___See left.___

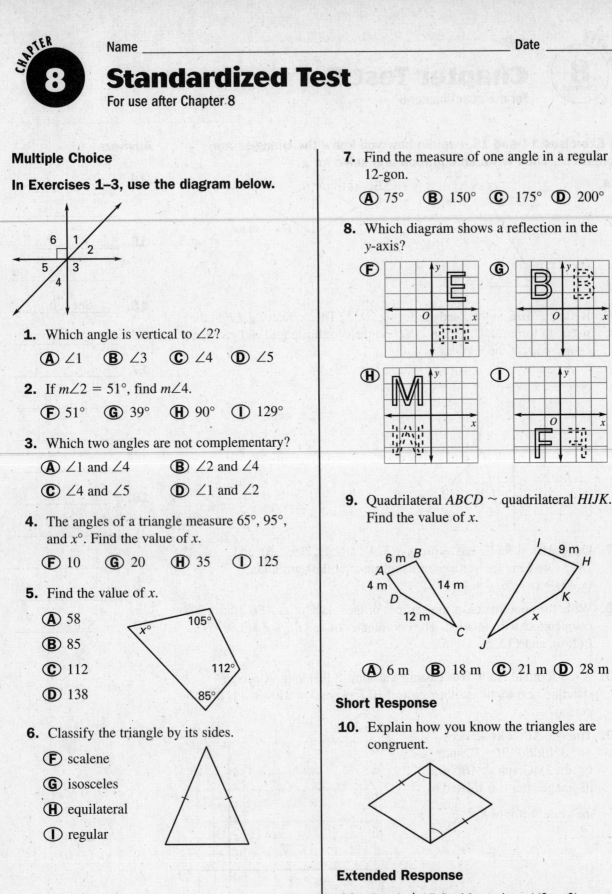

Multiple Choice

In Exercises 1–3, use the diagram below.

1. Which angle is vertical to ∠2?

Ⓐ ∠1   Ⓑ ∠3   Ⓒ ∠4   Ⓓ ∠5

2. If $m\angle 2 = 51°$, find $m\angle 4$.

Ⓕ 51°   Ⓖ 39°   Ⓗ 90°   Ⓘ 129°

3. Which two angles are not complementary?

Ⓐ ∠1 and ∠4   Ⓑ ∠2 and ∠4

Ⓒ ∠4 and ∠5   Ⓓ ∠1 and ∠2

4. The angles of a triangle measure 65°, 95°, and x°. Find the value of x.

Ⓕ 10   Ⓖ 20   Ⓗ 35   Ⓘ 125

5. Find the value of x.

Ⓐ 58
Ⓑ 85
Ⓒ 112
Ⓓ 138

6. Classify the triangle by its sides.

Ⓕ scalene
Ⓖ isosceles
Ⓗ equilateral
Ⓘ regular

7. Find the measure of one angle in a regular 12-gon.

Ⓐ 75°   Ⓑ 150°   Ⓒ 175°   Ⓓ 200°

8. Which diagram shows a reflection in the y-axis?

Ⓕ   Ⓖ

Ⓗ   Ⓘ

9. Quadrilateral ABCD ~ quadrilateral HIJK. Find the value of x.

Ⓐ 6 m   Ⓑ 18 m   Ⓒ 21 m   Ⓓ 28 m

Short Response

10. Explain how you know the triangles are congruent.

Extended Response

11. Graph △ABC with vertices A(2, −3), B(5, −6), and C(4, 1). Translate the triangle using (x, y) → (x − 3, y + 2). Then graph the image and label its vertices.

Alternative Assessment and Math Journal

For use after Chapter 8

Journal　**1.** In the chapter, you learned about five special types of quadrilaterals. Describe each of those types.

Multi-Step Problem　**2.** You are hired by an architectural firm to work with some house plans. You copy one of the house plans onto a coordinate plane as shown below.

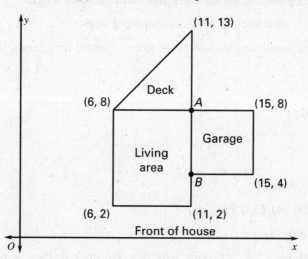

a. Assuming that the living area and the garage are rectangular, find the coordinates of points *A* and *B*.

b. Classify the shape of the deck as an *acute triangle*, an *obtuse triangle*, or a *right triangle*.

c. Of the living area, deck, and garage, which are *polygons*?

d. Are any of the areas shown *regular polygons*?

e. Identify any lines of symmetry for the plan of the house above.

f. If you want your plan to be three times as large, you can dilate it by a scale factor of three. Find the coordinates of the deck after you perform this dilation.

g. The family planning to build the house decides that they would rather live across the street which is represented by the *x*-axis on the grid. Explain which transformation technique you could use to adjust the original plan.

h. After performing the transformation in part (g), how would the coordinates of the points on the new plan correspond to the coordinates on the plan drawn above?

Name _____ Date _____

Alternative Assessment Rubric

For use after Chapter 8

Journal Solution

1. Complete answers should include the following:

   • A *trapezoid* is a quadrilateral with exactly one pair of parallel sides.

   • A *parallelogram* is a quadrilateral with both pairs of opposite sides parallel.

   • A *rhombus* is a parallelogram with four sides of equal length.

   • A *rectangle* is a parallelogram with four right angles.

   • A *square* is a parallelogram with four sides of equal length and four right angles.

Multi-Step Problem Solution

2. **a.** $A(11, 8)$, $B(11, 4)$

   b. right triangle

   c. all of them

   d. the garage

   e. no lines of symmetry

   f. (18, 24), (33, 24), (33, 39)

   g. reflection in the *x*-axis

   h. The *x*-coordinates for each point would be the same as they were before the reflection; however, the *y*-coordinates would be the opposites of those before the reflection.

Multi-Step Problem Rubric

4 The student makes no more than one error and is able to explain how the coordinates of the points of an image reflected in the *x*-axis relate to the coordinates before the reflection.

3 The student makes no more than one error but is unable to adequately explain the relationship between the coordinates of the points before and after the reflection.

2 The student makes between two and four errors.

1 The student makes more than four errors.

Name _____ Date _____

Quiz 1

For use after Lessons 9.1–9.4

Evaluate the square root.

1. $\sqrt{121}$ **2.** $-\sqrt{100}$ **3.** $\sqrt{169}$

Solve the equation.

4. $x^2 = 625$ **5.** $y^2 - 14 = 67$

Graph each pair of numbers on the number line. Then complete the statement with <, >, or =.

6. $\sqrt{\dfrac{9}{16}}$ ____ $\dfrac{3}{4}$

0.2 0.4 0.6 0.8 1.0

7. -4 ____ $-\sqrt{18}$

−4.4 −4.2 −4.0 −3.8 −3.6

Find the unknown length. Round to the nearest tenth, if necessary.

8.

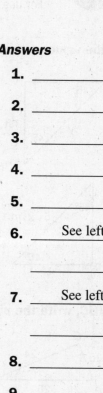

9.

10. Your uncle is planting an 8-foot tall tree. He ties support wires to the tree, 1 foot from the top, and ties them to posts on the ground, 4 feet from the trunk of the tree. How long is each wire to the nearest tenth of a foot?

Determine whether the numbers form a Pythagorean triple.

11. 14, 48, 50 **12.** 17, 21, 27

Answers

1. _____

2. _____

3. _____

4. _____

5. _____

6. _____See left._____

_____

7. _____See left._____

_____

8. _____

9. _____

10. _____

11. _____

12. _____

Name _____ Date _____

Quiz 2

For use after Lessons 9.5 and 9.6

Find the value of each variable. Give exact answers.

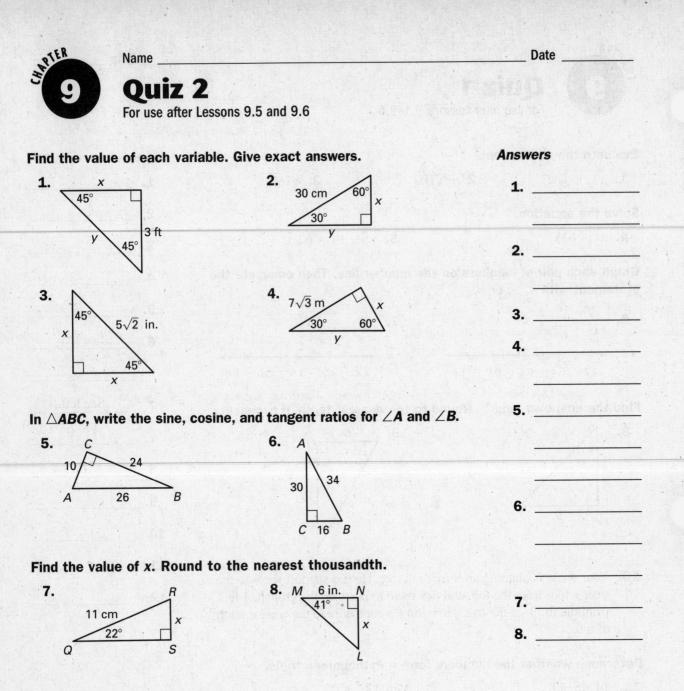

Answers

1. _____

2. _____

3. _____

4. _____

5. _____

6. _____

7. _____

8. _____

1.

2.

In △ABC, write the sine, cosine, and tangent ratios for ∠A and ∠B.

5.

6.

Find the value of x. Round to the nearest thousandth.

7.

8.

Name _____ Date _____

Chapter Test A
For use after Chapter 9

Find the two square roots of the number.

1. 36

2. 400

Use a calculator to evaluate the square root. Round to the nearest tenth.

3. $\sqrt{32}$

4. $-\sqrt{65}$

In Exercises 5 and 6, solve the equation.

5. $x^2 = 169$

6. $c^2 + 21 = 85$

7. A square patio has an area of 324 square feet. How long are the sides of the patio?

Tell whether the number is *rational* or *irrational*. Explain your reasoning.

8. $\sqrt{\dfrac{1}{9}}$

9. $\sqrt{7}$

10. $\dfrac{\sqrt{4}}{5}$

Graph the pair of numbers on a number line. Then complete the statement with <, >, or =.

11. $\dfrac{4}{5}$ _____ $\sqrt{\dfrac{16}{25}}$

12. 4 _____ $\sqrt{14}$

Let *a* and *b* represent the lengths of the legs of a right triangle, and let *c* represent the length of the hypotenuse. Find the unknown length.

13. $a = 15, b = 20, c =$ _____

14. $a = 16, b =$ _____, $c = 34$

Answers

1. _____

   _____

2. _____

   _____

3. _____

4. _____

5. _____

6. _____

7. _____

8. _____

   _____

   _____

   _____

9. _____

   _____

   _____

   _____

10. _____

    _____

11. _____See left._____

    _____

12. _____See left._____

    _____

13. _____

14. _____

15. Find the perimeter of the triangle.

10 m

24 m

Answers

In Exercises 16 and 17, determine whether the numbers form a Pythagorean triple.

16. 40, 42, 58   **17.** 18, 80, 84

18. You are standing 15 feet from the base of a cliff. Using a laser range finder, you measure the distance to the top of the cliff to be 25 feet. How high is the cliff?

In Exercises 19 and 20, find the value of the variable. Give exact answers.

19.

17 ft   60°   y
30°
$17\sqrt{3}$ ft

20.

11 cm   11 cm
45°   45°
y

15. _____

16. _____

17. _____

18. _____

19. _____

20. _____

21. _____

22. _____

23. _____

24. _____

In Exercises 21–23, use △LMN to find the ratio for ∠L.

21. sine ratio

22. cosine ratio

23. tangent ratio

L

20   29

N   21   M

24. Find the value of x. Round your answer to the nearest thousandth.

x   15 mm
20°

Name _____ Date _____

Chapter Test B

For use after Chapter 9

Approximate the square root to the nearest whole number.

1. $\sqrt{62}$

2. $\sqrt{130}$

Solve the equation.

3. $a^2 = 1$

4. $b^2 - 72 = 49$

5. $c^2 + 51 = 87$

6. $d^2 - 1500 = 2100$

In Exercises 7 and 8, graph the pair of numbers on a number line. Then complete the statement with <, >, or =.

7. 6 ____ $\sqrt{40}$

```
  +--+--+--+--+--+--+--+--+--+-->
  5.5        6.0        6.5
```

8. $\dfrac{2}{3}$ ____ $\sqrt{\dfrac{8}{18}}$

```
  +--+--+--+--+--+--+--+-->
  -1        0         1
```

9. Order the numbers 3.5, $\sqrt{10}$, $\sqrt{12}$, and $\dfrac{17}{5}$ from least to greatest.

Find the unknown length. Round to the nearest tenth, if necessary.

10.

12 m   20 m
     a

11.

11 in.

c   12 in.

In Exercises 12 and 13, determine if the triangle with the given side lengths is a right triangle.

12. $a = 12, b = 22, c = 30$

13. $a = 32, b = 60, c = 68$

14. A tree house is 10 feet up in a tree. A ladder that leans against the tree and leads to the tree house door is 12 feet long. How far from the base of the tree is the bottom of the ladder? Round to the nearest tenth.

Answers

1. _____
2. _____
3. _____
4. _____
5. _____
6. _____
7. ___See left.___

   _____
8. ___See left.___

   _____
9. _____
10. _____
11. _____
12. _____
13. _____
14. _____

Chapter Test B

For use after Chapter 9

Find the perimeter and area of the triangle.

Answers

15.

34 cm

16 cm

16.

30 in.

40 in.

Find the value of each variable. Give exact answers.

17.

45°

6 m

y

45°

x

18.

y   60°

5 in.

30°

x

19.

30°

x   15 ft

60°

y

20.

x   x

45°   45°

$7\sqrt{2}$ cm

In Exercises 21 and 22, use △KLM to write the sine, cosine, and tangent ratios for the given angle.

21. ∠K

22. ∠L

M

14   48

K   50   L

Find the value of x. Round your answer to the nearest thousandth.

23.

x

12 cm

38°

24.

x

24 mm

25°

15. _____

_____

16. _____

_____

17. _____

_____

18. _____

_____

19. _____

_____

20. _____

21. _____

_____

22. _____

23. _____

24. _____

Name _____ Date _____

Chapter Test C

For use after Chapter 9

Find the square root.

1. $-\sqrt{256}$

2. $\sqrt{\dfrac{36}{121}}$

In Exercises 3–6, solve the equation. Round to the nearest hundredth, if necessary.

3. $w^2 + 14 = 63$

4. $x^2 + 21 = 117$

5. $18 + y^2 = 21$

6. $z^2 - 51 = 147$

7. Find two square roots of 2.56.

8. You are building a square enclosure for your dog. You want it to have 225 square feet of space. How many feet of fencing should you buy?

In Exercises 9 and 10, evaluate the expression when $x = 3$, $y = 2$ and $c = 6$. Tell whether the result is _rational_ or _irrational_.

9. $\sqrt{xy - c}$

10. $\sqrt{c^2 - y^2}$

11. Order the numbers -3.6, $-\dfrac{5}{4}$, $-\sqrt{\dfrac{16}{9}}$, and $-\sqrt{15}$ from least to greatest.

Let a and b represent the lengths of the legs of a right triangle, and let c represent the length of the hypotenuse. Find the unknown length.

12. $a = 4$, $b =$ _____, $c = 8.5$

13. $a = 1.8$, $b = 8$, $c =$ _____

Answers

1. _____

2. _____

3. _____

4. _____

5. _____

6. _____

7. _____

8. _____

9. _____

10. _____

11. _____

12. _____

13. _____

14. Determine whether a triangle with side lengths of 2.1, 7.2, and 7.5 inches is a right triangle.

15. A right triangle has a hypotenuse of 14.6 meters and a leg of 9.6 meters. Find the length of the unknown leg. Then find the area and perimeter.

16. A right triangle has an area of 15.6 square feet and a leg of 3.9 feet. What is its perimeter?

In Exercises 17–20, find the value of each variable. Give exact answers.

17.

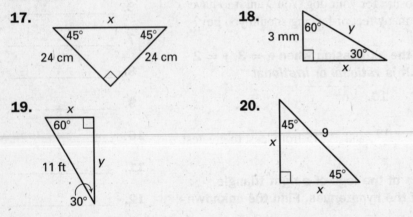

18.

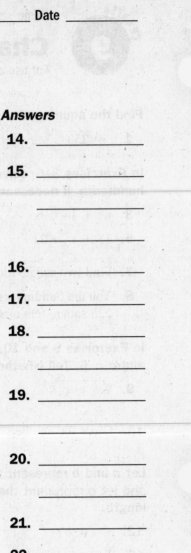

19.

20.

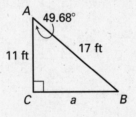

21. You have a square tablecloth with sides that are 50 inches long. You fold the tablecloth between two opposite corners to form a triangle. What is the length of the fold? Round your answer to the nearest tenth.

22. Use trigonometric ratios to write two equations that could be used to find the value of a. Find the value of a to the nearest hundredth of a foot.

Answers

14. _____

15. _____

_____

_____

16. _____

17. _____

18. _____

19. _____

_____

20. _____

21. _____

22. _____

_____

Name _____   Date _____

Standardized Test

For use after Chapter 9

Multiple Choice

1. Approximate $\sqrt{235}$ to the nearest whole number.

(A) 14   (B) 15   (C) 16   (D) 17

2. Solve $x^2 - 8 = 56$.

(F) ± 6 (G) ± 7 (H) ± 8 (I) ± 9

3. The area of a square rug is 196 square feet. What is its perimeter?

(A) 28 feet   (B) 32 feet

(C) 56 feet   (D) 98 feet

4. Which number is irrational?

(F) $\frac{1}{3}$ (G) $\sqrt{9}$ (H) $\sqrt{\frac{4}{25}}$ (I) $\sqrt{5}$

5. Which statement is true?

(A) $\sqrt{17} < 4$ (B) $\sqrt{\frac{4}{16}} = \frac{1}{4}$

(C) $\sqrt{28} > 5$ (D) $9 < \sqrt{78}$

6. The hypotenuse of a right triangle has a length of 34 mm, and one of the legs has a length of 16 mm. What is the length of the other leg?

(F) 25 mm   (G) 27 mm

(H) 30 mm   (I) 32 mm

7. Find the values of x and y.

(A) $x = 9\sqrt{3}, y = 18$

(B) $x = 18, y = 9\sqrt{3}$

(C) $x = 4.5\sqrt{3}, y = 4.5$

(D) $x = 4.5, y = 4.5\sqrt{3}$

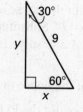

8. In $\triangle ABC$, find $\tan A$.

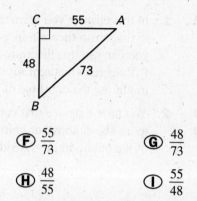

(F) $\frac{55}{73}$ (G) $\frac{48}{73}$

(H) $\frac{48}{55}$ (I) $\frac{55}{48}$

Short Response

9. You and a friend are vacationing at the same location. You drop your friend off at the airport, then drive due south 120 miles, then due east 250 miles to the vacation spot. Your friend flies directly to the vacation spot. How many miles did she travel? Round to the nearest tenth of a mile.

Extended Response

10. Find the value of x in the triangle below. Show your work. Round to the nearest thousandth.

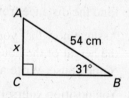

Name _____ Date _____

Alternative Assessment and Math Journal

For use after Chapter 9

Journal   **1.** In this chapter you learned about the Pythagorean theorem. Explain the Pythagorean theorem in your own words. Explain under what conditions you can use this theorem. Also explain what the converse of the Pythagorean theorem says. Give an example of a situation in which you might use the converse of the Pythagorean theorem.

Multi-Step Problem   **2.** You have a device that can measure the angle from any horizontal surface to an object above or below that surface. You decide to estimate the height of the public library. A sketch is shown below:

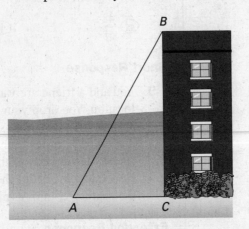

a. You measure angle *A* to be 60°. What is the measure of angle *B*?

b. The distance from the device to the base of the library is 43.3 feet. What is the height of the library?

c. Find the distance from *A* to *B*.

d. Assume now that you wish to estimate the height of a house. Let *h* be the height of the house and *d* be the distance from the device to the base of the house. Write an expression for the tangent of angle *A*.

e. You position yourself 33 feet from the house and the angle from the ground to the top of the house is 47°. Substitute these values in your formula for the tangent of angle *A* and solve for *h* to find the height of the house.

f. Find the distance from the top of the house to the device.

g. Explain why you could not simply use the Pythagorean theorem to find the height in part (e).

h. Your French pen pal, Pierre, wants to photograph the Eiffel Tower. To do this, he wants to find a point on the ground where the angle to the top of the 300-meter tower is 38°. How far from the center of the tower's base should he stand? Explain how you found your answer.

Alternative Assessment Rubric
For use after Chapter 9

Journal Solution

1. Complete answers should include the following:

- Correct explanation of the Pythagorean theorem

- Recognition that the Pythagorean theorem can be applied to right triangles only

- Explanation of the converse of the Pythagorean theorem: If you have a triangle with sides of lengths a, b, and c such that $c^2 = a^2 + b^2$, then the triangle must be a right triangle.

- Example showing a correct use of the converse of the Pythagorean theorem

Multi-Step Problem Solution

2. a. 30°

  b. 75.0 ft

  c. 86.6 ft

  d. $\tan A = \dfrac{h}{d}$

  e. 35.4 ft

  f. 48.4 ft

  g. You only knew the length of one of the sides of the triangle. To apply the Pythagorean theorem, you would need to know lengths of two of the sides to solve for the third.

  h. about 384 m; Use the equation $\tan 38° = \dfrac{300}{d}$ and solve for d, the distance.

Multi-Step Problem Rubric

4 The student makes no computational error and is able to apply the tangent ratio in the context of the Eiffel Tower problem. The explanation of the solution is correct and complete.

3 The student uses the tangent ratio but makes a slight computational error. The explanation of the solution is correct and complete.

2 The student uses the target ratio but makes a significant computational error. The explanation is only partially correct and/or complete.

1 The student uses the incorrect trigonometric ratio. The explanation is incorrect and/or incomplete.

Name _____ Date _____

Quiz 1

For use after Lessons 10.1–10.3

In Exercises 1 and 2, find the area of the parallelogram or trapezoid.

Answers

1.

4 in.

8 in.

2.

8 cm

3 cm

14 cm

1. _____

2. _____

3. ___ See left. ___

_____

4. ___ See left. ___

3. Sketch a parallelogram with a base of 9 inches and a height of 6 inches. Then find its area.

5. _____

6. _____

7. _____

4. Sketch a trapezoid with bases of 6 meters and 8 meters, and a height of 5 meters. Then find its area.

8. _____

9. _____

_____

_____

_____

In Exercises 5–7, find the area of the circle with the given radius or diameter. Use 3.14 for π.

5. $r = 12$ m   **6.** $d = 18$ yd   **7.** $r = 5.2$ cm

10. _____

_____

8. Find the radius of a circle with an area of 706.5 square centimeters. Use 3.14 for π.

_____

_____

Classify the solid. Tell whether it is a polyhedron. If so, count the number of faces, edges, and vertices.

_____

_____

9.

10.

Name _____ Date _____

Quiz 2

For use after Lessons 10.4–10.7

Find the surface area and volume of the solid. Round to the nearest tenth. Use 3.14 for π.

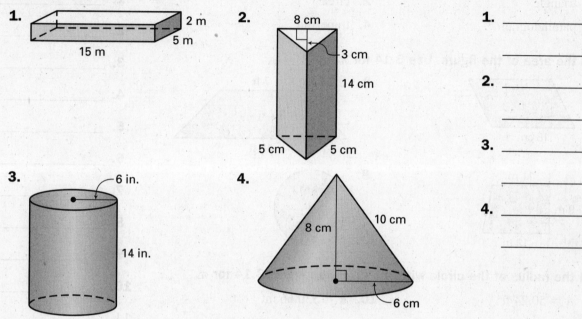

1.

2 m
5 m
15 m

2.

8 cm
3 cm
14 cm
5 cm   5 cm

3.

6 in.
14 in.

4.

8 cm   10 cm
6 cm

Answers

1. _____

_____

2. _____

_____

3. _____

_____

4. _____

_____

Name _____ Date _____

Chapter Test A

For use after Chapter 10

Write the area formula for the figure.

1. triangle

2. circle

3. parallelogram

4. trapezoid

Find the area of the figure. Use 3.14 for π.

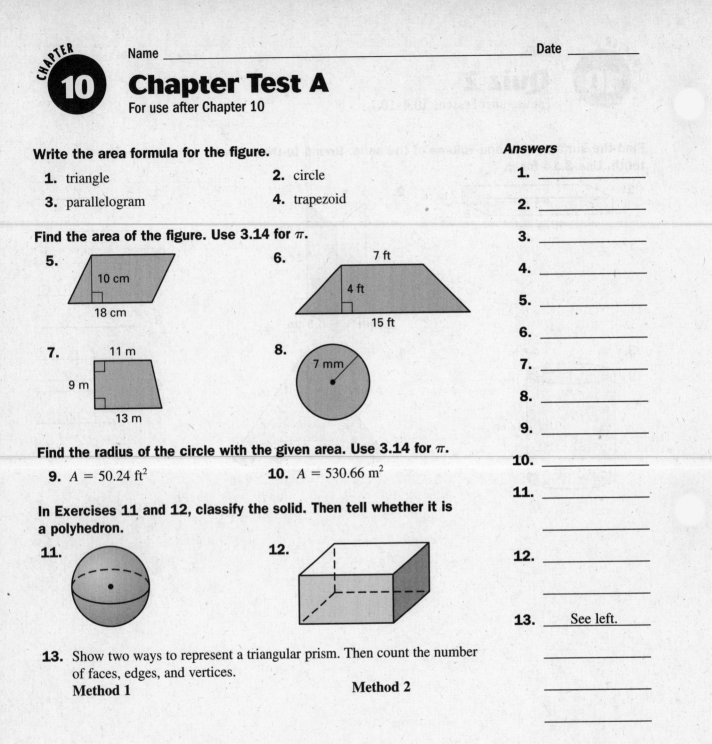

5.

10 cm

18 cm

6.

7 ft

4 ft

15 ft

7.

11 m

9 m

13 m

8.

7 mm

Find the radius of the circle with the given area. Use 3.14 for π.

9. $A = 50.24 \text{ ft}^2$

10. $A = 530.66 \text{ m}^2$

In Exercises 11 and 12, classify the solid. Then tell whether it is a polyhedron.

11.

12.

13. Show two ways to represent a triangular prism. Then count the number of faces, edges, and vertices.

Method 1   Method 2

Answers

1. _____

2. _____

3. _____

4. _____

5. _____

6. _____

7. _____

8. _____

9. _____

10. _____

11. _____

12. _____

13. _____ See left.

_____

_____

_____

_____

Name _____ Date _____

Chapter Test A

For use after Chapter 10

In Exercises 14 and 15, draw a net for the solid. Then find the surface area of the solid.

14.

7 in.

3 in.

15.

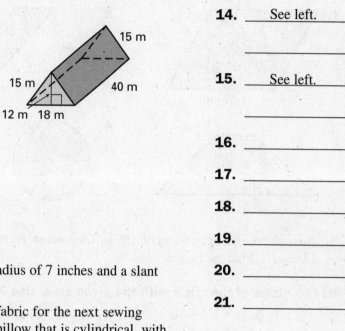

15 m

15 m

40 m

12 m   18 m

Answers

14. _____See left._____

_____

15. _____See left._____

_____

16. _____

17. _____

18. _____

19. _____

20. _____

21. _____

16. Find the surface area of a cone with a radius of 7 inches and a slant height of 11 inches.

17. A home economics teacher is ordering fabric for the next sewing project. Each student will be making a pillow that is cylindrical, with a diameter of 8 inches and a length of 14 inches. How many square inches of fabric will be used for each pillow?

Find the volume of the solid.

18.

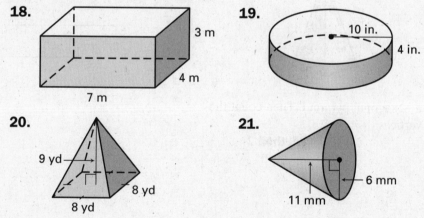

3 m

4 m

7 m

19.

10 in.

4 in.

20.

9 yd

8 yd

8 yd

21.

6 mm

11 mm

McDougal Littell Math, Course 3   **121**
Chapter 10   Assessment Book

Name _____ Date _____

Chapter Test B
For use after Chapter 10

In Exercises 1–4, find the area of the figure. Use 3.14 for π.

Answers

1.

13 cm

18 cm

2.

6 mm

8 mm

3 mm

3.

4 yd

6 yd

17 yd

4.

21 m

5. A parallelogram has an area of 195 square meters. Its base is 13 meters. Find the height.

Find the radius of the circle with the given area. Use 3.14 for π.

6. $A = 113.04 \text{ in.}^2$ 7. $A = 706.5 \text{ m}^2$

In Exercises 8 and 9, classify the solid. Then tell whether it is a polyhedron.

8.

9.

10. Show two ways to represent a hexagonal pyramid. Then count the number of faces, edges, and vertices.

Method 1   **Method 2**

1. _____

2. _____

3. _____

4. _____

5. _____

6. _____

7. _____

8. _____

9. _____

_____

10. ___See left.___

_____

_____

_____

Name _____ Date _____

Chapter Test B

For use after Chapter 10

In Exercises 11–14, find the surface area of the solid. Round to the nearest tenth, if necessary. Use 3.14 for π.

Answers

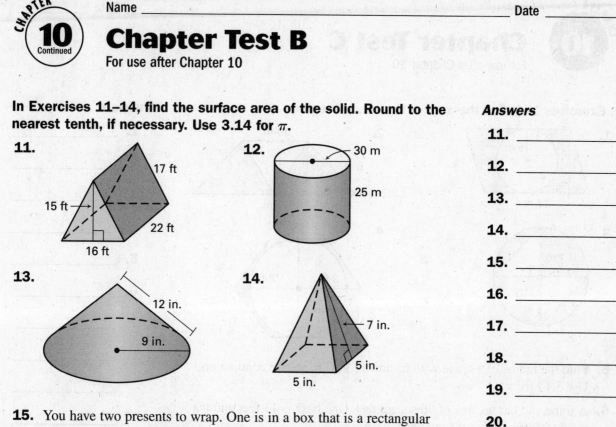

11. _____

12. _____

13. _____

14. _____

15. _____

16. _____

17. _____

18. _____

19. _____

20. _____

11. 17 ft / 15 ft / 22 ft / 16 ft

12. 30 m / 25 m

13. 12 in. / 9 in.

14. 7 in. / 5 in. / 5 in.

15. You have two presents to wrap. One is in a box that is a rectangular prism measuring 10 inches by 6 inches by 12 inches. The other is in a hat box that is a cylinder. It has a diameter of 16 inches and a height of 7 inches. Which box has the greater surface area?

In Exercises 16–19, find the volume of the solid.

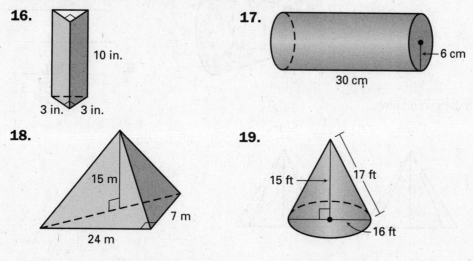

16. 10 in. / 3 in. 3 in.

17. 6 cm / 30 cm

18. 15 m / 7 m / 24 m

19. 15 ft / 17 ft / 16 ft

20. You are filling a baby pool with water. The pool is a cylinder with a diameter of 6 feet and a height of 1.5 feet. If you fill the pool $\frac{2}{3}$ of the way full, how many cubic feet of water are in the pool?

Name _____ Date _____

Chapter Test C
For use after Chapter 10

In Exercises 1–4, find the area of the shaded region.

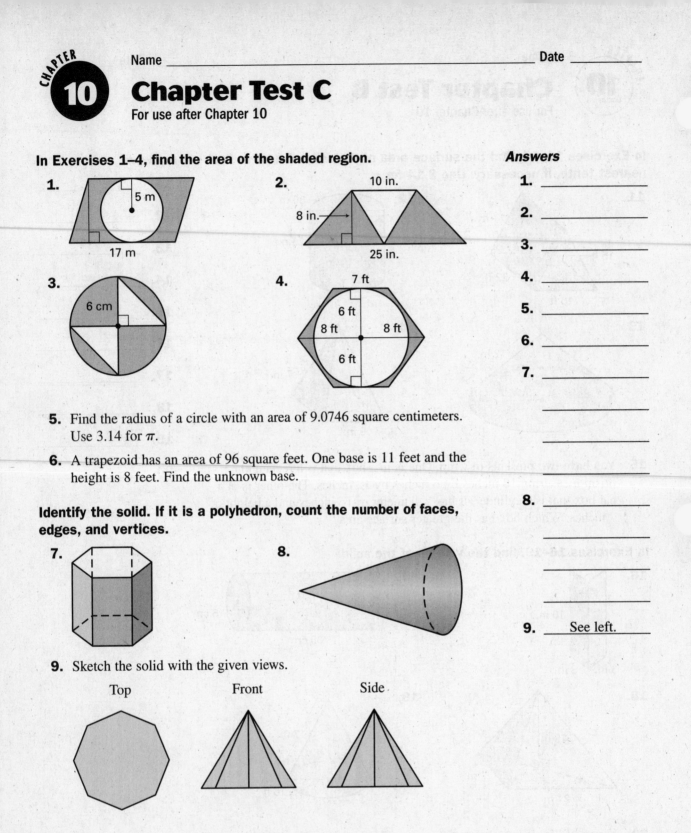

1.

5 m

17 m

2.

10 in.

8 in.

25 in.

3.

6 cm

4.

7 ft

6 ft

8 ft   8 ft

6 ft

Answers

1. _____

2. _____

3. _____

4. _____

5. _____

6. _____

7. _____

5. Find the radius of a circle with an area of 9.0746 square centimeters.
Use 3.14 for π.

6. A trapezoid has an area of 96 square feet. One base is 11 feet and the
height is 8 feet. Find the unknown base.

**Identify the solid. If it is a polyhedron, count the number of faces,
edges, and vertices.**

7.

8.

8. _____

_____

_____

_____

9. Sketch the solid with the given views.

Top   Front   Side

9. ____See left.____

Name _____ Date _____

Chapter Test C
For use after Chapter 10

10. A school is soundproofing a band room with insulating tiles. The room is rectangular and is 30 feet long, 40 feet wide, and 12 feet high. All four walls, the floor, and the ceiling will be covered, but a window that is 10 feet long by 4 feet high will not be covered. How many square feet of tiling is needed? If each tile is 8 inches by 8 inches, how many tiles should be ordered?

Find the surface area and volume of the solid. Round to the nearest tenth, if necessary. Use 3.14 for π.

11.

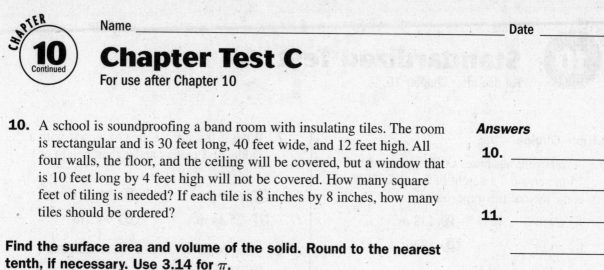

15 in.   7 in.

12.

17 ft
22 ft
8 ft

13.

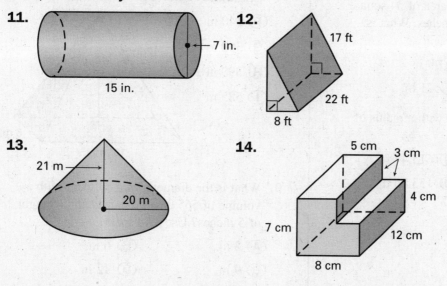

21 m   20 m

14.

5 cm   3 cm
4 cm
7 cm
12 cm
8 cm

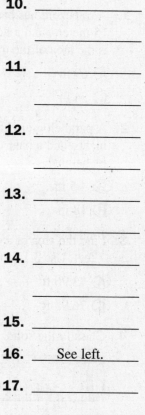

Answers

10. _____

_____

11. _____

_____

12. _____

_____

13. _____

_____

14. _____

_____

15. _____

16. ___See left.___

17. _____

_____

In Exercises 15–17, use the following information. A square pyramid has a volume of 1280 cubic meters. The base side lengths are 16 meters.

15. Find the perpendicular height of the pyramid.

16. Sketch the pyramid, and label the known measurements.

17. Find the slant height of the pyramid using the Pythagorean theorem. Then find the surface area of the pyramid.

Standardized Test

For use after Chapter 10

Multiple Choice

1. A trapezoid has bases of 8 meters and 15 meters, and a height of 6 meters. What is the area of the trapezoid?

  Ⓐ 69 m²   Ⓑ 138 m²

  Ⓒ 84 m²   Ⓓ 53 m²

2. A parallelogram has an area of 54 square inches and a base of 6 inches. What is its height?

  Ⓕ 4.5 in.   Ⓖ 9 in.

  Ⓗ 18 in.   Ⓘ 21 in.

3. Find the area of a circle with a radius of 7 feet. Use 3.14 for π.

  Ⓐ 43.96 ft²   Ⓑ 615.44 ft²

  Ⓒ 76.93 ft²   Ⓓ 153.86 ft²

4. Classify the solid.

  Ⓕ cylinder   Ⓖ cone

  Ⓗ circle   Ⓘ sphere

5. How many edges does a rectangular pyramid have?

  Ⓐ 5   Ⓑ 6   Ⓒ 8   Ⓓ 12

6. How many square feet of material would be needed to make the tent below?

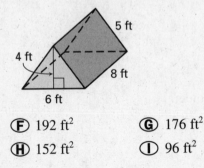

  Ⓕ 192 ft²   Ⓖ 176 ft²

  Ⓗ 152 ft²   Ⓘ 96 ft²

7. What is the surface area of a cone with a radius of 3 meters and a slant height of 7 meters?

  Ⓐ 65.94 m²   Ⓑ 219.8 m²

  Ⓒ 25.84 m²   Ⓓ 94.2 m²

8. What is the volume of the rectangular pyramid?

  Ⓕ 540 m³

  Ⓖ 360 m³

  Ⓗ 390 m³

  Ⓘ 585 m³

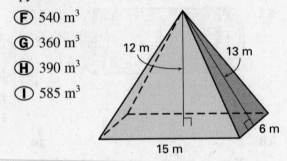

9. What is the diameter of a cylinder with a volume of 565.2 cubic inches and a height of 5 inches? Use 3.14 for π.

  Ⓐ 3 in.   Ⓑ 6 in.

  Ⓒ 9 in.   Ⓓ 12 in.

Short Response

10. Wax cylinder records were used to record music in the late 1800s. A wax record was a 4-inch long hollow cylinder with a 2-inch diameter. Music was recorded on grooves around the outside of the curved surface of the cylinder. Make a sketch and find the area of the curved recording surface.

Extended Response

11. Find the surface area and volume of a cube with sides of 4 centimeters. Then double the side lengths and find the surface area and volume. Write a ratio of the original surface area to the new surface area, and the original volume to the new volume. Simplify the ratios.

Name _____ Date _____

Alternative Assessment and Math Journal

For use after Chapter 10

Journal

1. Explain how to find the areas of parallelograms, trapezoids, and circles. Include a drawing, the algebraic formula for area, and an example for each type of figure.

Multi-Step Problem

2. The following is a three-dimensional sketch of the tent you take on a camping trip:

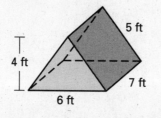

5 ft

4 ft

7 ft

6 ft

a. Count the number of faces of the tent.

b. Count the number of edges of the tent.

c. Count the number of vertices of the tent.

d. Find the volume of the tent.

e. Find the surface area of the tent.

f. Sketch a net for the tent.

g. You make a cone shaped paper cup. Its height is 10 centimeters and its diameter is 8 centimeters. What volume of water will the cup hold?

h. You pour a drink of water from your canteen. Your canteen is the shape of a cylinder with a diameter of 20 centimeters and a height of 6 centimeters. What volume of water does the canteen hold?

i. What is the surface area of your canteen?

j. Explain why all of the following terms are correct ways of referring to the tent: *solid*, *polyhedron*, and *prism*.

Journal Solution

1. Complete answers should include the following:

- Explanations for how to find areas of parallelograms, trapezoids, and circles

- Drawing, algebraic formula for area, and example for each type of figure

Multi-Step Problem Solution

2. a. 5

b. 9

c. 6

d. 84 ft^3

e. 136 ft^2

f.

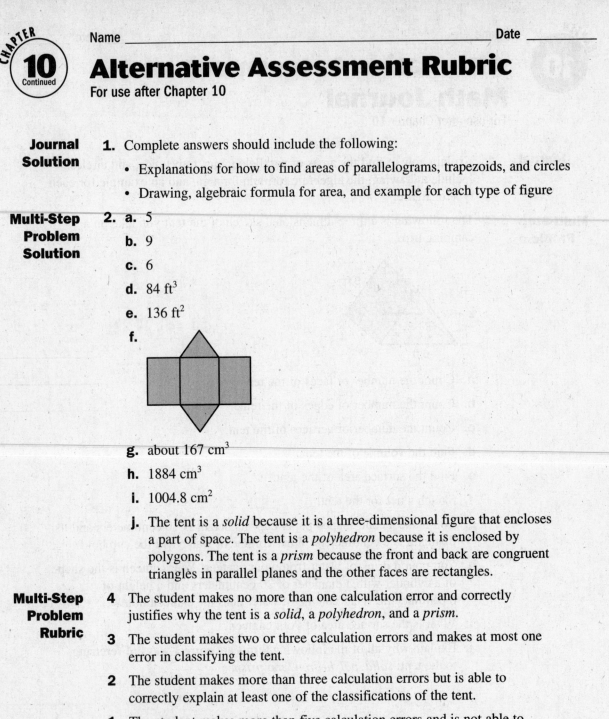

g. about 167 cm^3

h. 1884 cm^3

i. 1004.8 cm^2

j. The tent is a *solid* because it is a three-dimensional figure that encloses a part of space. The tent is a *polyhedron* because it is enclosed by polygons. The tent is a *prism* because the front and back are congruent triangles in parallel planes and the other faces are rectangles.

Multi-Step Problem Rubric

4 The student makes no more than one calculation error and correctly justifies why the tent is a *solid*, a *polyhedron*, and a *prism*.

3 The student makes two or three calculation errors and makes at most one error in classifying the tent.

2 The student makes more than three calculation errors but is able to correctly explain at least one of the classifications of the tent.

1 The student makes more than five calculation errors and is not able to correctly explain any of the classifications of the tent.

Name _____ Date _____

Unit 3 Test
For use after Chapters 8–10

Find the measure of the numbered angles.

Answers

1.

2.

1. _____

2. _____

3. _____

4. _____

5. _____

In Exercises 3–5, classify the polygon.

6. _____

3.

4.

5.

7. _____

6. Find the sum of the angle measures in a 15-gon.

Use the diagram. Quadrilateral *ABCD* ≅ quadrilateral *MNQP*.

8. _____

7. Name four pairs of congruent angles.

8. Name four pairs of congruent sides.

9. _____

10. _____

11. _____

Tell whether the figures are reflections of each other.

9.

10.

12. _____

13. _____

Solve the equation.

11. $x^2 = 81$

12. $y^2 - 11 = 156$

14. _____

Tell whether the number is *rational* or *irrational*. Explain your reasoning.

13. $\dfrac{3}{5}$

14. $\sqrt{10}$

15. $\sqrt{\dfrac{4}{36}}$

15. _____

Find the unknown length.

16.

17.

16. _____

17. _____

UNIT 3 Continued

Unit 3 Test

For use with Chapters 8–10

In Exercises 18 and 19, find the value of each variable. Give exact answers.

Answers

18.

19.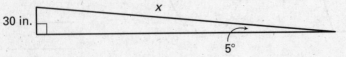

18. _____

19. _____

_____

20. **20.** Your class is constructing a handicap access ramp as a service project for school. The ramp is shown in the diagram. Find the length x of the ramp to the nearest inch.

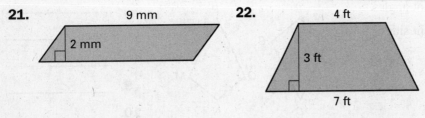

20. _____

21. _____

22. _____

23. _____

24. _____

In Exercises 21 and 22, find the area of the parallelogram or trapezoid.

21.
9 mm
2 mm

22.
4 ft
3 ft
7 ft

25. _____

23. Find the area of a circle with a radius of 8 meters. Use 3.14 for π.

24. Classify the solid. Then count the number of faces, edges, and vertices.

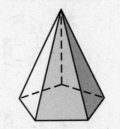

26. _____

Find the surface area and volume of the solid.

25.
12 in.
8 in.   6 in.

26.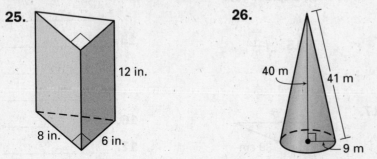
40 m   41 m
9 m

Name _____ Date _____

Cumulative Test

For use after Chapters 1-10

In Exercises 1 and 2, evaluate the expression.

Answers

1. $49 - 16 \times 2 \div 4$

2. $\left[(8 - 3)^3 - 15\right] \div 11$

3. You are buying 4 books and 3 magazines. The cost of one book is x dollars. The cost of one magazine is y dollars. Write a variable expression to represent the cost of the books and magazines. Then find the total purchase price if books cost $5.50 each and magazines cost $3.25.

4. The area of a rectangle is 112 square inches, and the width is 8 inches. Find the length.

Find the sum, difference, product, or quotient.

5. $17 - 21$

6. $31 - (-24)$

7. $-7(-6)(-5)$

8. $\dfrac{-325}{-25}$

Simplify the expression by combining like terms.

9. $9y - 11x - (-12y) + 5x$

10. $13x - 17 - (-3x) - 4(2x - 8)$

In Exercises 11 and 12, solve the equation.

11. $w - 18 = 24$

12. $\dfrac{z}{9} = -$

13. The admission price to a seminar being offered at a local hotel is $35 per person. The hotel charges the company putting on the seminar $515 to rent the conference room. Write and solve an equation to find the number of people that need to attend for the company to make a $1200 profit.

Solve and graph the inequality.

14. $x - 72 < 51$

```
←——+——+——+——+——→
   122  123  124  125
```

15. $-6x \geq 42$

```
←+——+——+——+——+——+——+——+——+——→
 -10 -9 -8 -7 -6 -5 -4 -3 -2
```

1. _____

2. _____

3. _____

_____

4. _____

5. _____

6. _____

7. _____

8. _____

9. _____

10. _____

11. _____

12. _____

13. _____

_____

14. _____

_____ See left.

15. _____

_____ See left.

16. Find the width of a rectangle with a length of 21 feet and an area of 357 square feet.

Find the greatest common factor and the least common multiple.

17. 18, 20, 24

18. $45a^7b^6, 30a^5b^9$

In Exercises 19 and 20, write the fraction in simplest form.

19. $\dfrac{121}{165}$

20. $\dfrac{72mn}{36n}$

21. Order the fractions $\dfrac{5}{8}, \dfrac{11}{14}, \dfrac{2}{3},$ and $\dfrac{5}{7}$ from least to greatest.

Simplify the expression. Write your answer as a power using only positive exponents.

22. $x^9 \cdot x^6$

23. $b^{-5} \cdot b^{-4}$

24. $\dfrac{24m^3n^5}{6m^6n}$

Solve the equation.

25. $\dfrac{3}{4}w = 2\dfrac{5}{6}$

26. $m - 1\dfrac{2}{3} = \dfrac{5}{12}$

27. $-\dfrac{11}{15} + y = -2\dfrac{1}{15}$

28. $z \div \dfrac{1}{5} = \dfrac{2}{3}$

29. $19 - 4x = -11$

30. $3(5k - 11) = 12k + 6$

Find the sum, difference, product, or quotient.

31. $13.6(1.75)$

32. $0.6336 \div 0.072$

33. $-25.86 - (-14.961)$

In Exercises 34–36, write the mixed number as a decimal or write the decimal as a fraction.

34. $1\dfrac{7}{18}$

35. $0.\overline{08}$

36. 2.04

37. The circumference of a circle is 87.92 centimeters. What is its radius?

Answers

16. _____

17. _____

_____

18. _____

_____

19. _____

20. _____

21. _____

22. _____

23. _____

24. _____

25. _____

26. _____

27. _____

28. _____

29. _____

30. _____

31. _____

32. _____

33. _____

34. _____

35. _____

36. _____

37. _____

Name _____ Date _____

Cumulative Test
For use after Chapters 1–10

38. Translate the sentence into an inequality. Then solve the inequality.
11 more than 3 times a number is at least 9 less than 5 times a number.

39. Write the equivalent rate: $\dfrac{142 \text{ miles}}{3 \text{ hours}} = \dfrac{?}{1 \text{ day}}$.

In Exercises 40 and 41, solve using a percent proportion.

40. What is 45% of 64?

41. 703 is what percent of 380?

42. You put $350 in a savings account that pays simple interest at a 4.5% annual rate. How much interest will you earn in 3 years?

43. Find the percent of increase or decrease.

original amount: 165   new amount: 200

In Exercises 44 and 45, classify the triangle by its side lengths.

44.   **45.**

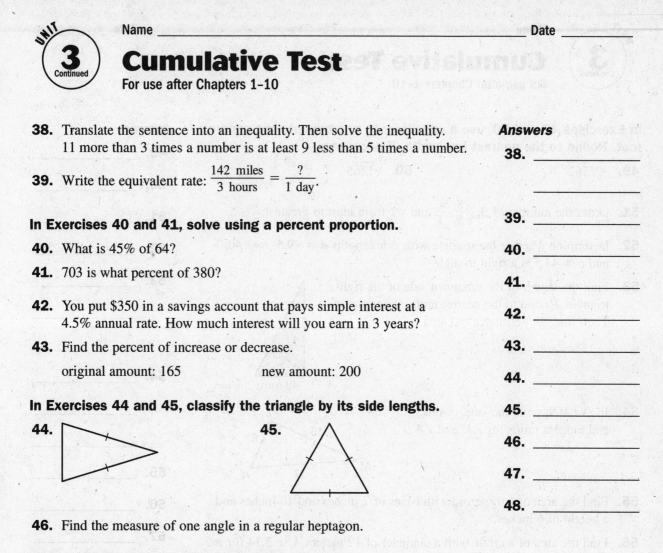

46. Find the measure of one angle in a regular heptagon.

Write and solve an equation to find the value of x.

47.   **48.**

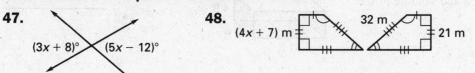

$(3x + 8)°$ $(5x - 12)°$ $(4x + 7)$ m   32 m   21 m

Answers

38. _____

_____

39. _____

40. _____

41. _____

42. _____

43. _____

44. _____

45. _____

46. _____

47. _____

48. _____

Cumulative Test

For use after Chapters 1–10

In Exercises 49 and 50, use a calculator to approximate the square root. Round to the nearest hundredth, if necessary.

49. $-\sqrt{562}$

50. $\sqrt{1265}$

51. Order the numbers 1.3, $\sqrt{\dfrac{8}{5}}$, $\dfrac{4}{3}$, and $\sqrt{2}$ from least to greatest.

52. Determine whether the triangle with side lengths $a = 19.5$, $b = 40$, and $c = 44.5$ is a right triangle.

53. Find the length of the unknown side of the right triangle. Round to the nearest tenth, if necessary. Then find the perimeter and area.

102 mm

48 mm

54. In △ *LMN*, write the sine, cosine, and tangent ratios for ∠*M* and ∠*N*.

L

15

8

M

17

N

55. Find the area of a trapezoid with bases of 7 inches and 10 inches and a height of 6 inches.

56. Find the area of a circle with a diameter of 12 meters. Use 3.14 for π

57. Find the surface area and volume of the rectangular prism.

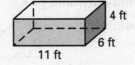

4 ft

6 ft

11 ft

Answers

49. _____

50. _____

51. _____

52. _____

53. _____

_____

_____

54. _____

_____

_____

55. _____

56. _____

57. _____

_____

CHAPTER 11

Name _____ Date _____

Quiz 1

For use after Lessons 11.1–11.4

In Exercises 1 and 2, tell whether the relation is a function.

1. (1, 3), (2, 6), (5, 4),
(−1, 5), (3, 2), (2, 4)

2.

Input	3	5	7	9
Output	1	3	5	7

Answers

1. _____

2. _____

3. Write a function rule
that relates x and y.

Input x	0	1	2	3
Output y	0	−3	−6	−9

3. _____

4. ____See left.____

4. The table shows the numbers of students playing soccer in an indoor
league in different years. Make a scatter plot of the data. What
conclusions can you make?

Year	1999	2000	2001	2002	2003
Students	24	36	50	55	62

_____

_____

5. _____

_____

Indoor Soccer League

Students: 70, 60, 50, 40, 30, 20, 10, 0
Year: 1999, 2000, 2001, 2002, 2003

_____

_____

6. _____

_____

_____

In Exercises 5 and 6, list three solutions of the equation.

5. $y = 4x - 5$

6. $y = \frac{1}{2}x + 2$

7. ____See left.____

7. Graph the linear equation $y = 2x + 1$.

Name _____ Date _____

Quiz 2

For use after Lessons 11.5–11.8

Find the intercepts of the graph of the equation.

1. $y = 4x - 2$ **2.** $2x + 3y = 12$

Find the slope of the line passing through the points.

3. $(6, 3), (4, 7)$ **4.** $(12, 9), (7, 3)$

Find the slope and *y*-intercept of the graph of the equation. Then graph the equation.

5. $y = x - 3$ **6.** $3x + 5y = 15$

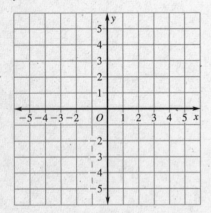 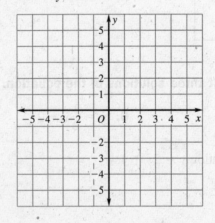

Graph the inequality.

7. $y \geq 3$ **8.** $3x + 4y \geq 12$

Answers

1. _____

   _____

2. _____

   _____

3. _____

4. _____

5. _____

   See left.

6. _____

   See left.

7. _____ See left.

8. _____ See left.

Chapter Test A

For use after Chapter 11

In Exercises 1 and 2, tell whether the relation is a function.

1. $(-5, -1), (-3, 2), (-1, 0), (1, 3), (3, 5), (5, 6)$

2.

Input x	5	7	-5	-7
Output y	2	2	2	2

3. Complete the table of values for the function rule $3x + y = 7$.

Input x	-2	0	2	4
Output y				

Tell whether x and y have a *positive relationship*, a *negative relationship*, or *no relationship*.

4.

5.

Rewrite the equation in function form. Then tell whether the ordered pair is a solution of the equation.

6. $4x + y = 7; (3, -5)$

7. $-6x + 3y = 9; (2, -9)$

Graph the linear equation.

8. $y = x + 6$

9. $y = 6$

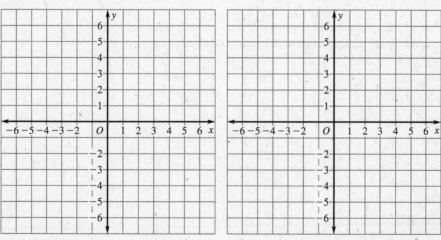

Answers

1. _____

2. _____

3. _See left._

4. _____

5. _____

6. _____

_____

7. _____

_____

8. _See left._

9. _See left._

In Exercises 10 and 11, identify the *x*-intercept and the *y*-intercept.

Answers

10.

11.

10. _____

_____

11. _____

12. Does the graph in Exercise 10 have a *positive slope*, a *negative slope*, or a *zero slope*?

13. Find the slope of the line passing through the points (3, 8) and (1, 3).

Rewrite the equation in slope-intercept form.

14. $3x + y = -1$ **15.** $12x - 3y = 15$

Find the slope and *y*-intercept of the graph of the equation.

16. $y = 2x - 7$ **17.** $y = 8 - 3x$

Tell whether the point is a solution of the inequality $7x - 2y \geq 16$.

18. $(1, -4)$ **19.** $(8, 4)$ **20.** $(4, 6)$

Graph the inequality.

21. $y < 4x - 3$ **22.** $y \geq -2x + 5$

12. _____

13. _____

14. _____

15. _____

16. _____

_____

17. _____

_____

18. _____

19. _____

20. _____

21. _____ See left. _____

22. _____ See left. _____

CHAPTER

11

Chapter Test B

For use after Chapter 11

1. Tell whether the relation is a function. Explain your answer.
$(-6, -3), (-4, -2), (-2, 0), (2, 0), (4, -2), (6, -3)$

In Exercises 2 and 3, write a function rule that relates the input x and the output y.

2.

x	−2	0	2	4
y	4	0	−4	−8

3.

x	0	1	2	3
y	1	4	7	10

4. Make a scatter plot of the data. What conclusion can you make?

Year	1994	1996	1998	2000	2002
Price per gallon of heating oil ($)	1.20	1.45	1.60	1.75	1.98

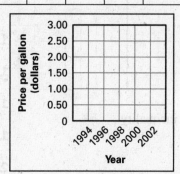

Tell whether the ordered pair is a solution of the equation $y = -4x + 3$.

5. $(-2, -5)$ **6.** $(3, -9)$ **7.** $\left(\frac{1}{2}, 1\right)$

Graph the linear equation.

8. $x = -3$ **9.** $y = 3x - 2$

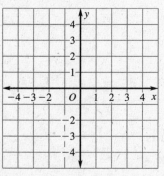 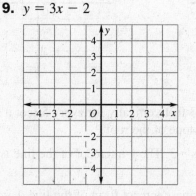

Find the intercepts of the graph of the equation.

10. $y = -6$ **11.** $y = 3x + 9$

Answers

1. _____

2. _____

3. _____

4. _____See left._____

_____

_____

5. _____

6. _____

7. _____

8. _____See left._____

9. _____See left._____

10. _____

_____

11. _____

_____

Name _____ Date _____

Chapter Test B
For use after Chapter 11

Find the slope of the line passing through the points.

12. $(5, 7), (-2, -3)$ **13.** $(6, 3), (4, 7)$

In Exercises 14 and 15, find the slope and *y*-intercept of the graph of the equation. Then graph the equation.

14. $y = -2x + 5$ **15.** $y = \frac{4}{5}x - 3$

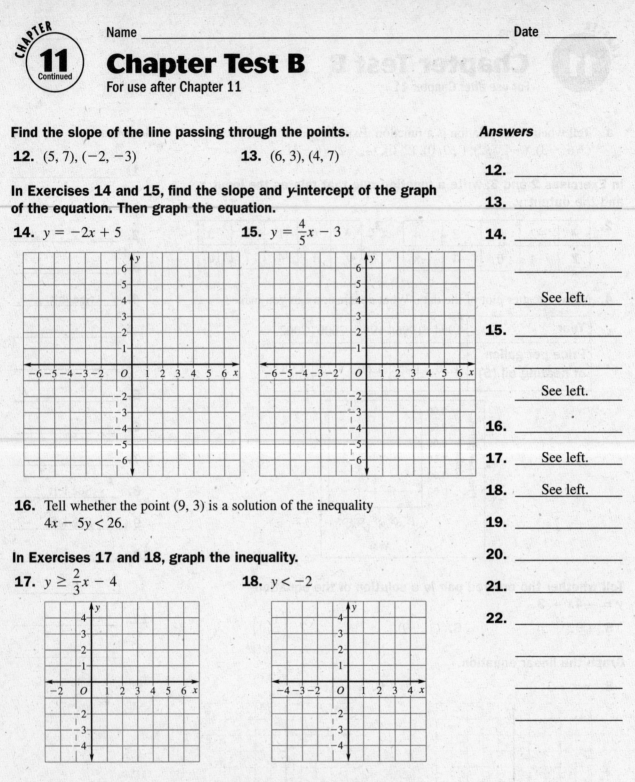

16. Tell whether the point $(9, 3)$ is a solution of the inequality $4x - 5y < 26$.

In Exercises 17 and 18, graph the inequality.

17. $y \geq \frac{2}{3}x - 4$ **18.** $y < -2$

Answers

12. _____

13. _____

14. _____

_____

_____ See left.

15. _____

_____ See left.

16. _____

17. _____ See left.

18. _____ See left.

19. _____

20. _____

21. _____

22. _____

_____

_____

_____

19. The roof of a house rises 3 feet vertically for every 5 feet it runs horizontally. What is the slope of the roof?

20. The *x*-intercept of a line is -3. The *y*-intercept of the line is 6. What is the slope of the line?

21. What is the equation in slope-intercept form of the line described in Exercise 20?

22. Use the concept of slope to explain whether the three points $A(3, 1)$, $B(-2, 2)$, and $C(-4, 4)$ can all be points on the same line.

140 **McDougal Littell Math, Course 3**
Chapter 11 Assessment Book

Name _____ Date _____

Chapter Test C

For use after Chapter 11

In Exercises 1 and 2, write a function rule that relates the input *x* to the output *y*.

1.

x	−2	0	2	4
y	5	1	−3	−7

2.

x	−3	0	3	6
y	−4	−2	0	2

3. Logan gets $.10 for every newspaper he delivers during the week, and $.15 for each Sunday paper. Is the money he earns a function of the number of papers delivered? Explain below.

Describe the type of relationship you might expect for the given data.

4. The amount owed on a car loan and the length of time you have owned the car

5. The height of a student and his or her shoe size

In Exercises 6–8, tell whether the ordered pair is a solution of the equation $14x - 7y = 28$.

6. $(1.2, -1.6)$ **7.** $\left(\frac{3}{4}, 5\frac{1}{2}\right)$ **8.** $(-0.7, -5.4)$

9. An airport is 1250 feet above sea level. An airplane taking off is ascending at a rate of 125 feet per second. Graph the equation $h = 125s + 1250$, where h is the height of the plane above sea level, and s is the time in seconds. Use the graph to estimate the time it will take the plane to reach an altitude of 4500 feet.

Find the intercepts of the graph of the equation.

10. $y = 5x - 3$ **11.** $y = \frac{2}{3}x - 4$

Answers

1. _____

2. _____

3. _____See left._____

4. _____

5. _____

6. _____

7. _____

8. _____

9. _____See left._____

_____

10. _____

_____

11. _____

_____

12. The three points $A(2, 5)$, $B(4, 2)$, and
$C(-2, 1)$ are vertices of a triangle.
Plot and connect the points. Then
find the slope of each side of
the triangle.

Answers

12. _____See left._____

_____

_____

In Exercises 13 and 14, write the equation of the graph in slope-intercept form.

13.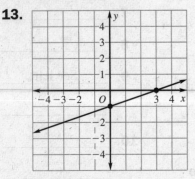

14.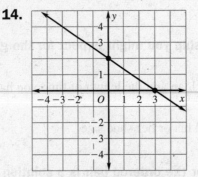

13. _____

14. _____

15. _____

16. _____See left._____

17. _____

15. Write the inequality represented
by the graph at the right.

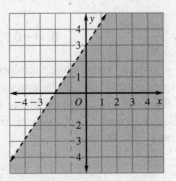

In Exercises 16 and 17, use the following information. A pickup truck can haul 1200 pounds of cargo. A rancher is buying grain in 50-pound bags and hay bales that weigh 60 pounds each.

16. Graph the inequality $50x + 60y \leq 1200$
to show the possible ways to load the
pickup truck.

17. Use the graph to estimate the greatest
number of hay bales he can buy if he
buys 5 bags of grain.

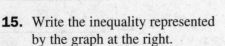

Name _____ Date _____

Standardized Test

For use after Chapter 11

Multiple Choice

1. The function rule $y = 2x - 1$ relates x and y in which set of ordered pairs?

Ⓐ $(-1, -3), (0, 1), (2, 5)$

Ⓑ $(1, 3), (2, 5), (8, 9)$

Ⓒ $(0, -1), (2, 3), (3, 5)$

Ⓓ $(1, 1), (3, 2), (-1, 0)$

2. Describe the relationship shown in the data.

Input x	2	4	7	10
Output y	12	9	8	7

Ⓕ positive   Ⓖ negative

Ⓗ none   Ⓘ not enough information

3. Which of the ordered pairs is a solution of the equation $y = 7x - 13$?

Ⓐ $(-2, 1)$ Ⓑ $(-13, 0)$

Ⓒ $(3, 8)$ Ⓓ $(-1, -6)$

4. Which is the best description of the graph of $-7x + 2y = 42$?

Ⓕ a vertical line

Ⓖ a horizontal line

Ⓗ a line slanted downward from left to right

Ⓘ a line slanted upward from left to right

5. What is the slope of the line passing through the points $(-7, -5)$ and $(-3, 1)$?

Ⓐ $\frac{2}{3}$ Ⓑ $\frac{3}{2}$ Ⓒ $\frac{1}{2}$ Ⓓ $\frac{2}{5}$

6. What is the slope of the line $5x - 3y = 15$?

Ⓕ $\frac{5}{3}$ Ⓖ $-\frac{5}{3}$ Ⓗ 5   Ⓘ -5

7. What is the y-intercept of the line $-3x + 4y = 12$?

Ⓐ $\frac{3}{4}$ Ⓑ $-\frac{3}{4}$ Ⓒ 3   Ⓓ -3

8. Which inequality is represented by the graph?

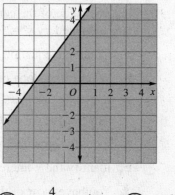

Ⓕ $y < \frac{4}{3}x + 4$ Ⓖ $y \leq \frac{4}{3}x + 4$

Ⓗ $y > \frac{4}{3}x + 4$ Ⓘ $y \geq \frac{4}{3}x + 4$

Short Response

9. Find the intercepts of the graph of $3y - 7x = 42$.

Extended Response

10. Some students raised $320 for their school library. The library can buy books for $16 each or videos for $25 each. The inequality $16x + 25y \leq 320$ models the situation, where x is the number of books and y is the number of videos. Graph the inequality. Then explain how to use the graph to find the maximum number of videos the library can buy if it buys 14 books.

Name _____ Date _____

Alternative Assessment and Math Journal

For use after Chapter 11

Journal   **1.** Explain in your own words what a *relation* is. Explain what a *function* is. Explain what is meant by the *domain* and *range* of a function. Give a real-life example of a function and specify the domain and range of the function. Also give a real-life example of a relation that is *not* a function and explain why it is not.

Multi-Step   **2.** You own a used car dealership. For a certain model of car, you determine
Problem   that the value of the car to your dealership x years after it is first sold is approximated by $y = -800x + 12{,}000$.

    a. Graph the equation of the line.

    b. What is the slope of the line?

    c. Is there a *positive relationship* or a *negative relationship* between the value of the car and its age?

    d. Identify the x-intercept of the line and interpret its value.

    e. Identify the y-intercept of the line and interpret its value.

    f. You have a car of the given model on your lot that is 6 years old. Use the equation to approximate the car's value.

    g. You are told that the value of a car of the given model, based on its age, is less than $6000. Give a range of values that could represent the age of the car.

    h. You are selling a 3 year old model. Your dealership is running a special by giving an 8 percent discount off the usual value of the vehicle. How much would you sell the car for?

    i. A different car model is worth $15,000 when it is brand new and is worth $8025 when it is 9 years old. Explain how you would find the equation of the line that gives the value of this model after it is x years old. Write the equation.

CHAPTER 11 Continued
Alternative Assessment Rubric
For use after Chapter 11

Journal Solution

1. Complete answers should include the following:

   • Explanation of what a relation is

   • Explanation of what a function is

   • Explanation of domain and range of a function

   • Real-life example of function with domain and range specified

   • Real-life example of relation that is not a function with reasoning explained

Multi-Step Problem Solution

2. a.
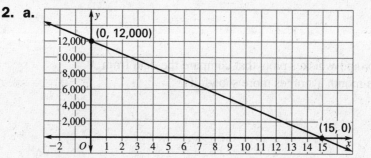

   b. -800

   c. negative relationship

   d. 15; The vehicle has no value when it is 15 years old.

   e. 12,000; The vehicle is valued at $12,000 when it is brand new.

   f. $7200

   g. The vehicle is older than 7.5 years ($x > 7.5$).

   h. $8832

   i. The $15,000 represents the y-intercept. The slope can be computed using the two points (0, 15,000) and (9, 8025). Then write the slope-intercept form, $y = mx + b$; $y = -775x + 15,000$.

Multi-Step Problem Rubric

4 The student makes no more than one mistake and has a clearly written algorithm for finding the equation of the line in the written exercise.

3 The student makes two or three mistakes and/or does not have a complete algorithm for finding the equation of the line in the written exercise.

2 The student makes four or five mistakes and/or the student is unable to write an algorithm to find the equation of the line in the written exercise.

1 The student makes more than five mistakes.

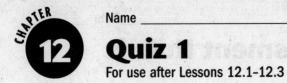

Quiz 1

For use after Lessons 12.1–12.3

1. The data show the January and February snowfall accumulations in inches for a town for 10 years. Make an ordered double stem-and-leaf plot comparing the data.

Find the median value of the data.

January: 28, 32, 24, 17, 28, 11, 9, 36, 31, 30
February: 29, 16, 21, 39, 11, 27, 24, 34, 15, 22

2. Make a pair of box-and-whisker plots that compare the data from Question 1. Which month averages more snowfall?

3. There are 40 students riding a school bus: 12 are eighth-graders, 18 are seventh-graders, and 10 are sixth-graders. Decide whether a circle graph or a line graph would better represent the data. Then make the graph of your choice. Explain your choice.

Answers

1. _____See left._____

2. _____See left._____

_____

3. _____See left._____

_____

_____

Quiz 2

For use after Lesson 12.4–12.8

1. A child can choose one stuffed animal. She can choose from a dog or a bear. Each comes in brown, gray, or white. Make a tree diagram to show the possible choices for the stuffed animal.

2. At a banquet, the dinner menu offers a choice of beef, chicken, or fish and either a pasta, potato, or vegetable side dish. Use the counting principle to find how many choices are possible.

3. A relay team has 5 people. In how many different ways can the 5 people run in the race?

Evaluate the expression.

4. $_9C_4$ 5. $_7P_5$ 6. $_9P_2$

In Exercises 7–9, use the following information. A bag contains 4 red buttons, 6 green buttons, and 5 blue buttons.

7. Find the probability: You choose a green button, replace it, then choose a blue button.

8. Find the probability: What are the odds you randomly choose a red button?

9. You randomly choose a blue button, keep it, and then choose another blue button.

Answers

1. ____See left.____

2. _____

3. _____

4. _____

5. _____

6. _____

7. _____

8. _____

9. _____

In Exercises 1–3, write the number as it would appear in a stem-and-leaf plot. Identify the stem and the leaf.

Answers

1. 76   **2.** 121   **3.** 15.1

1. _____

   _____

4. The stem-and-leaf plot shows the weights, in pounds, of first graders in a class. What are the weights of the lightest and heaviest students? What is the median weight?

```
3 | 8 9
4 | 2 4 5 6 7 7 9
5 | 0 1 3 5 8
6 | 0 0 2    Key: 6|0 = 60
```

2. _____

5. Make an ordered stem-and-leaf plot of the data. Then make a box-and-whisker plot of the data.
17 in., 22 in., 36 in., 19 in., 24 in., 27 in., 31 in., 26 in., 28 in.

3. _____

   _____

   _____

4. _____

In Exercises 6–8, convert the value into an angle measure for display in a circle graph.

5. _____See left._____

6. 16 out of 40   **7.** $\frac{2}{3}$ **8.** 45%

6. _____

7. _____

9. The table shows the results of a survey that asked students which of the four food types were their favorite. Make a circle graph to display the data.

8. _____

9. _____See left._____

Food	Percent
Pizza	40%
Hot dog	30%
Taco	10%
Hamburger	20%

Name _____ Date _____

Chapter Test A

For use after Chapter 12

10. There are three types of milk sold in a grocery store: fat-free, low-fat, and whole milk. The milk is available in either a $\frac{1}{2}$ gallon or a gallon container. Make a tree diagram to find the number of choices that are possible.

In Exercises 11–13, evaluate the expression.

11. 4!   **12.** $_6P_3$ **13.** $_7C_4$

14. Your parent leaves you a list of chores to complete. You are to dust the furniture, run the vacuum, wash the dishes, and put away the laundry. In how many different orders can the chores be completed?

15. You are having a sleep-over party and have 5 friends you could invite. You are only allowed to have 3 friends over. How many different choices of groups of friends do you have?

In Exercises 16 and 17, use the following information. You are given the probability that an event will occur. Find the probability that the event will not occur.

16. $P(A) = 62\%$ **17.** $P(A) = \frac{3}{8}$

18. There are 500 students in an auditorium. Of these students, 120 are eighth-graders. What are the odds of randomly selecting a student that is an eighth-grader?

In Exercises 19 and 20, use the following information. You randomly draw letter tiles from a bag containing the letters from the word PENNSYLVANIA. Find the probability. Then tell whether the events are independent or dependent.

19. You draw an A from the bag, replace it, and then draw an N.

20. You draw an N from the bag. Then, without replacing the first N, you draw another N.

Answers

10. _____See left._____

12. _____

13. _____

14. _____

15. _____

16. _____

17. _____

18. _____

19. _____

_____

20. _____

_____

Chapter Test B

For use after Chapter 12

In Exercises 1 and 2, make a stem-and-leaf plot of the data. Identify the interval that contains the greatest number of data values. Then make a box-and-whisker plot of the data.

1. 52, 47, 36, 41, 73, 65, 56, 39, 45

2. 13.6, 15.1, 13.3, 16.7, 14.7, 15.6, 14.3, 14.8, 12.6, 14.2

Answers

1. _____ See left. _____

    _____

    _____ See left. _____

2. _____ See left. _____

    _____

    _____ See left. _____

3. _____ See left. _____

4. _____ See left. _____

    _____

5. _____

3. The table shows the seasonal rainfall totals for a town. Make a circle graph to display the data.

Season	Inches of rainfall
Spring	10.5
Summer	3.9
Fall	7.2
Winter	8.4

4. There are three parks close to your home. At each park, you can go swimming, play football, rollerblade, or bike. Make a tree diagram to count the number of ways you could do an activity at a park.

5. A doll factory can make a doll with blonde, brown, red, or black hair and with brown, blue, green, or gray eyes. Use the counting principle to find the number of different dolls possible.

Name _____ Date _____

Chapter Test B
For use after Chapter 12

In Exercises 6–8, evaluate the expression.

6. $_7P_4$ **7.** $_9C_5$ **8.** $_{11}C_6$

Answers

9. A school orchestra has practiced 10 songs this year. The teacher needs to pick 5 songs for a concert. How many different arrangements could she pick?

10. An environmental organization is planting trees for Arbor Day. They will plant 4 different types of trees and will choose from 10 different varieties. Find the number of combinations of 4 tree varieties.

In Exercises 11–15, use the following information. You randomly draw letter tiles from a bag containing the letters from the word PROBABILITIES.

11. Find the probability that you choose a vowel.

12. Find the probability that you do not choose an I.

13. Find the odds in favor of choosing a B.

14. You randomly select a B. You replace it. Then you choose a T. Tell whether the events are *independent* or *dependent*. Then find the probability that both events occur.

15. You randomly pick an I. Then, without replacing the first I, you pick another I. Tell whether the events are *independent* or *dependent*. Then find the probability that both events occur.

6. _____

7. _____

8. _____

9. _____

10. _____

11. _____

12. _____

13. _____

14. _____

15. _____

CHAPTER 12

Chapter Test C
For use after Chapter 12

In Exercises 1–4, use the data that show the test scores on the first two tests of an eighth-grade science class.

Test 1: 75, 85, 76, 91, 100, 79, 83, 88, 86, 90, 93, 65, 77, 84, 86, 93, 73, 85, 89, 90

Test 2: 95, 87, 90, 70, 98, 84, 89, 77, 70, 90, 95, 84, 93, 81, 84, 98, 96, 74, 90, 73

1. Make an ordered double stem-and-leaf plot of the data.

2. What are the median test grades for Test 1 and Test 2?

3. Make a box-and-whisker plot for each test using the same number line.

4. Describe what the box-and-whisker plots show.

5. The data are the percents of people who indicated on a survey that they own the given types of animals. Display the data in an appropriate graph.

Animal	Response %
Dog	45
Cat	42
Bird	11
Horse	15
Snake	6
Other	7

6. A play is being performed on Friday, Saturday, and Sunday of two consecutive weekends. There are two performances each day, one at 2:00 P.M. and one at 7:00 P.M. Make a tree diagram to find the number of performances there will be.

Answers

1. _____See left._____

2. _____

   _____

3. _____See left._____

4. _____See left._____

5. _____See left._____

6. _____See left._____

CHAPTER 12 Continued

Chapter Test C

For use after Chapter 12

In Exercises 7–9, evaluate the expression.

7. $_{11}P_4$ **8.** $_{12}C_5$ **9.** $_{15}C_3$

10. There are 13 horses running in a race. In how many different ways can the horses place first, second, or third?

11. There are 15 children on a basketball team. The coach needs to pick 5 children to start the game. How many different 5-person teams can be chosen?

12. One state offers a zoo animal license plate that has 5 characters on it. The first three characters are letters and the last two are numbers. If each letter and number is used only once per plate, how many different license plates are possible? Is this a combination or permutation?

In Exercises 13–17, use the following information.

You randomly draw letter tiles from a bag containing the letters from the word INDEPENDENT.

13. What is the probability that a randomly chosen letter will be a D?

14. What are the odds in favor of a randomly chosen letter being an E?

15. What are the odds against a randomly chosen letter being a vowel?

16. You randomly draw an N. Then, without replacing the first letter, you pick a D. Tell whether the events are *independent* or *dependent*. Then find the probability that both events occur.

17. You randomly pick a T. You replace it. Then you pick an E. Find the probability that both events occur.

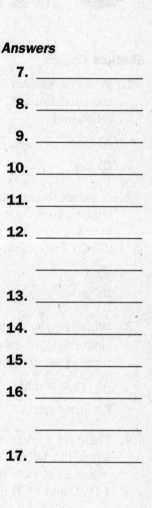

Answers

7. _____

8. _____

9. _____

10. _____

11. _____

12. _____

_____

13. _____

14. _____

15. _____

16. _____

_____

17. _____

Name _____ Date _____

Standardized Test
For use after Chapter 12

Multiple Choice

1. When the number 51 is plotted on a stem-and-leaf plot, the 5 is which of the following?

Ⓐ stem   Ⓑ leaf

Ⓒ key   Ⓓ median

2. A survey found that 3 out of 20 people enjoyed going to the dentist. Which angle measure should be used in a circle graph to display this quantity?

Ⓕ 3°   Ⓖ 15°

Ⓗ 30°   Ⓘ 54°

3. Which type of display would be most appropriate for data describing the monthly weight gain of a baby giraffe?

Ⓐ circle graph   Ⓑ bar graph

Ⓒ line graph   Ⓓ histogram

4. There are 5 DVDs and 6 CDs that you would like to buy. You only have money for one of each. How many different pairs of 1 DVD and 1 CD can you buy?

Ⓕ 6   Ⓖ 15   Ⓗ 30   Ⓘ 60

5. Sixteen students are competing in a cross-country race. In how many ways can they come in first, second, and third place?

Ⓐ 560   Ⓑ 1120

Ⓒ 3360   Ⓓ 4096

6. Three debate teams from a state are chosen to go to a national debate. If there are 12 teams in the state, how many different groups of three teams can be chosen to go to the national debate?

Ⓕ 220   Ⓖ 1320

Ⓗ 576   Ⓘ 1728

7. There are 7 yellow, 5 green, and 3 blue party hats in a bag. You randomly choose a yellow party hat and put it on. Then your friend randomly chooses a yellow party hat. What is the probability of both of you choosing a yellow party hat?

Ⓐ $\frac{1}{42}$ Ⓑ $\frac{1}{5}$

Ⓒ $\frac{49}{225}$ Ⓓ $\frac{42}{225}$

8. There are 100 students in a cafeteria. Of the 100 students, 36 of them are first-graders. What are the odds in favor of randomly picking out a first-grader?

Ⓕ 9 to 25   Ⓖ 25 to 9

Ⓗ 9 to 16   Ⓘ 16 to 9

Short Response

9. Calvin is getting dressed for a workout. He can choose from a T-shirt, a long-sleeved T-shirt, or a sweatshirt. He can wear long pants or shorts, and white or black running shoes. Use a tree diagram to find how many different outfits are possible.

Extended Response

10. The heights, in millimeters, of 10 seedlings from 2 seed types are shown.

Seed A: 56, 61, 48, 51, 59, 65, 49, 71, 69, 64
Seed B: 55, 63, 58, 47, 61, 46, 53, 47, 41, 59

Make box-and-whisker plots comparing the samples. Which seed type is, on average, taller?

Alternative Assessment and Math Journal

For use after Chapter 12

Journal

1. In your own words, describe how to make a box-and-whisker plot from a set of data. Be sure to include an explanation of how to compute each of the values needed to make this plot.

Multi-Step Problem

2. You decide to run for student council president. You are running against three other candidates. The class decides to have a debate to hear each candidate's views on a variety of issues. There are six issues to be discussed: the fall dance, the class mascot, the class colors, field trips, the end-of-the-year party, and school uniforms.

   a. If the debate is set up so that each issue is discussed, in how many different ways can they put the six debate issues on the agenda?

   b. Once the agenda is set, the order in which the candidates speak on the first issue is randomly selected. What is the probability that you are either the first or the last speaker for the first issue?

   c. You want to see how many possible arrangements there are for a first speaker and a first issue. For example, one possibility might be that your opponent Jada is selected to talk about the class mascot first. How many different combinations of speaker and issue are there to start the debate?

   d. What are the odds that you are the first speaker and the issue is the choice of class colors?

   e. If the selection of which of the candidates speaks first on each issue is random, what is the probability that you are chosen to speak first on both of the first two issues?

   f. In case the debate runs a little longer than expected, the organizers of the debate have decided that only four of the six issues will be debated. If the order in which the issues are presented does not matter, how many different groups of four issues can be selected?

   g. Is the event that the first topic to be discussed is the fall dance *independent* or *dependent* of the event that the second topic to be discussed is the end-of-the-year party? Explain your answer.

   h. Brooke and Carlos are the tallest of the six debaters. The school principal asks Brooke and Carlos to stay after the debate to help hang banners in the gymnasium for a basketball game. Is the selection of Brooke and Carlos considered to be a *random sample* or a *biased sample* of the four available candidates for president? Explain your answer.

Name _____ Date _____

Alternative Assessment Rubric

For use after Chapter 12

Journal Solution

1. Complete answers should include the following steps: Order the data from lowest value to highest value. Identify each of the extreme values (the lowest and highest values). Next, compute the median. This is the middle point of the data (if there is an odd number of values) or the average of the two middle numbers (if there is an even number of values). Using the median to divide the data set into two halves, find the quartiles. The lower quartile is the median of the lower half of the data. The upper quartile is the median of the upper half of the data. Then construct the box-and-whisker plot using these values.

Multi-Step Problem Solution

2. a. 720

b. $\frac{1}{2}$

c. 24

d. 1 to 23

e. $\frac{1}{16}$

f. 15

g. Dependent; knowing that the second topic is the end-of-the-year party affects the likelihood that the first topic will be the fall dance.

h. Biased sample; not all four of the candidates had an equal chance of being selected to stay after the debate to help.

Multi-Step Problem Rubric

4 Student answers all parts of the problem correctly, showing all work. The writing exercises are complete and well written.

3 Student answers all parts of the problem, but with one or two errors. All work is shown. The writing exercises are complete.

2 Student completes the problem. Student's work is complete but contains errors. The writing exercises are mostly complete but may contain incorrect statements or reasons.

1 Student's answers are incorrect or incomplete. The writing exercises are incomplete.

CHAPTER
13

Name _____ Date _____

Quiz 1

For use after Lessons 13.1–13.3

In Exercises 1–4, simplify the polynomial and write it in standard form.

1. $7x - 6 + 5x^2 + 3x^2$ **2.** $11y - 15 + y^2 - 6y$

3. $9m^2 - 6m + 5 + 2m + 3m^2$ **4.** $3(2p^2 + 7p) - 4p + 5p^2$

5. Find the value of $3x^2 - 7x + 11$ when $x = 5$.

In Exercises 6–9, find the sum or difference.

6. $(11b - 17) + (8b + 9)$ **7.** $(-6n + 15) - (3n - 8)$

8. $(7x^2 + 4x - 11) + (5x^2 - 8x - 15)$

9. $(9w + 5) - (3w + 7) + 4w$

10. Write a polynomial expression for the perimeter of the figure. Simplify the expression.

$x^2 - 3x + 2$

$x^2 - 3$

$5x + 4$

Simplify the expression.

11. $(6x^2)(-3x^3)$ **12.** $(5ab)^3$ **13.** $2m^2(3m^2 + 7)$

Answers

1. _____

2. _____

3. _____

4. _____

5. _____

6. _____

7. _____

8. _____

9. _____

10. _____

11. _____

12. _____

13. _____

Name _____ Date _____

Quiz 2

For use after Lessons 13.4–13.5

Find the product and simplify.

1. $(x + 8)(x - 11)$ **2.** $(m + 5)(m + 6)$

3. $(2y + 7)(y - 6)$ **4.** $(3a - 4)(4a - 7)$

Rewrite using function notation.

5. $y = 7x - 11$ **6.** $y = 6x^2 - 4x + 9$

Evaluate the function for $x = -2, -1, 0, 1,$ and 2. Then graph the function.

7. $f(x) = -2x^2$ **8.** $f(x) = x^2 - 7$

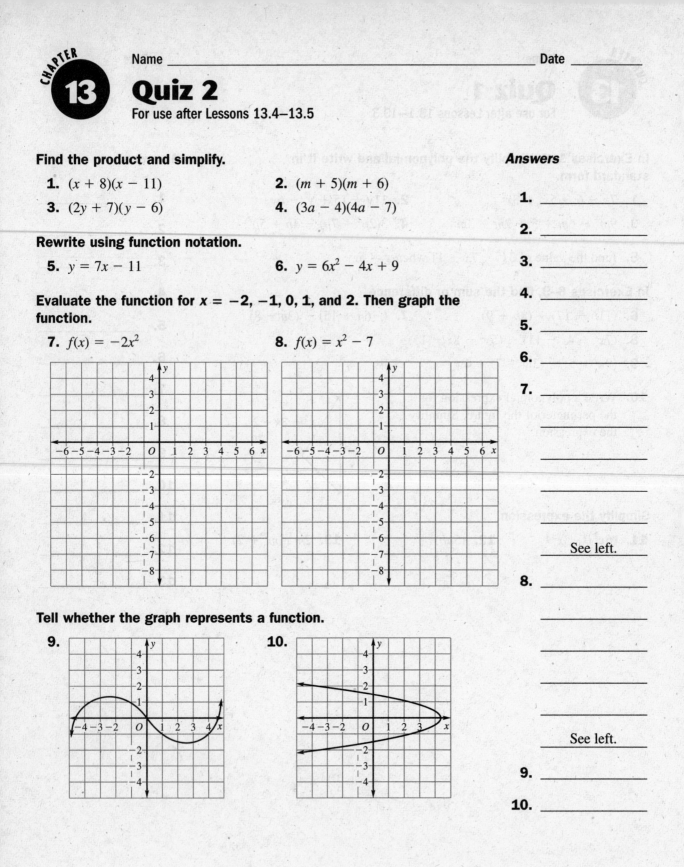

Tell whether the graph represents a function.

9.   **10.**

Answers

1. _____

2. _____

3. _____

4. _____

5. _____

6. _____

7. _____

_____

_____

See left.

8. _____

_____

_____

_____

See left.

9. _____

10. _____

13 Chapter Test A

For use after Chapter 13

Classify the polynomial as a *monomial*, a *binomial*, or a *trinomial*.

1. $x + 11$ **2.** $y^2 - 8y + 7$ **3.** $15a^2b$

Write the polynomial in standard form.

4. $7 - n^2 + 6n$ **5.** $w^2 + 11w^3 - 6 + 3w$

Simplify the polynomial and write it in standard form.

6. $7x - 9 + 4x$ **7.** $12 - 5m^2 - 2m^2 + 8m$

In Exercises 8–13, find the sum or difference.

8. $(11m + 8) - (3m - 4)$ **9.** $(9a + 7) + (7a + 11)$

10. $(-7w + 8) + (4w + 6)$ **11.** $(5y^2 + 3y - 6) - (2y^2 - 6y + 1)$

12. $(9x^3 - 5x + 2) + (-7x + 8)$ **13.** $(4y^2 - 11y) - (3y - 4)$

14. Write a polynomial expression for the perimeter of the triangle. Simplify the polynomial.

$3x - 5$ $4x + 1$
$2x + 7$

Simplify the expression.

15. $(4q)(3q^4)$ **16.** $(2x)^5$ **17.** $(m^5)^6$

18. $(-5k)^3$ **19.** $(3a^2)^4$ **20.** $5z(z^3 - 7)$

Answers

1. _____
2. _____
3. _____
4. _____
5. _____
6. _____
7. _____
8. _____
9. _____
10. _____
11. _____
12. _____
13. _____
14. _____
15. _____
16. _____
17. _____
18. _____
19. _____
20. _____

Find the product and simplify.

21. $5y(y + 8)$

22. $7m(3m - 4)$

23. $-9b(2b - 7)$

24. $(x + 2)(x + 11)$

25. $(r - 8)(r + 2)$

26. $(t - 6)(t - 4)$

Rewrite using function notation.

27. $y = 7x - 2$

28. $y = -6x^3$

Tell whether the graph represents a function.

29.

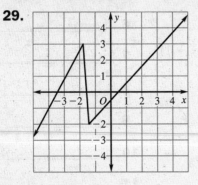

30.

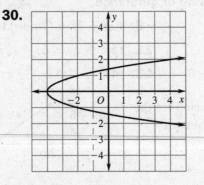

Complete the table of values. Then graph the function.

31. $f(x) = 2x^2$

x	−2	−1	0	1	2
f(x)					

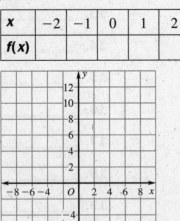

32. $f(x) = x^2 + 6$

x	−2	−1	0	1	2
f(x)					

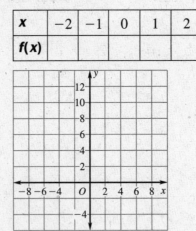

Answers

21. _____

22. _____

23. _____

24. _____

25. _____

26. _____

27. _____

28. _____

29. _____

30. _____

31. _____See left.____

32. _____See left.____

Name _____ Date _____

Chapter Test B

For use after Chapter 13

In Exercises 1 and 2, simplify the polynomial and write it in standard form.

1. $7x^2 - 3x + 4x^2 + x$ **2.** $9y - y^2 + 6y^2 + 8$

3. Find the value of $3x^2 - 7x + 5$ when $x = -3$.

4. Write a polynomial expression for the perimeter of the rectangle. Simplify the polynomial.

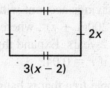

$2x$

$3(x - 2)$

Find the sum or difference.

5. $(5q^2 - 8q + 12) - (q^2 - 8)$ **6.** $(-m^2 + 6m - 3) + (4m^2 + m + 7)$

7. $(8n^3 + 3n^2 + 7) + (-n^2 + 11)$ **8.** $(6x^5 - 7x) + (-9x^5 + 8)$

9. $(2x^4 - x^2) - (x^4 - 3x^2 + 1)$ **10.** $(3y^2 - 2y + 8) + (3y^2 + 2y - 8)$

Simplify the expression.

11. $(3x^3)(7x^4)$ **12.** $(-q^5)(-3q^7)$ **13.** $5y(9y - 8)$

14. $(5z)^4$ **15.** $(-2wv)^3$ **16.** $(2n^3)(3n^2)^3$

17. You are cutting colored cardboard rectangles for the school art show. Each art piece will be placed on one of the rectangles so the outside of the rectangle forms a border or mat for the art piece. You are to cut the cardboard to fit artwork that is 3 times longer than it is wide. The mat should be 2 inches wide on each side. Write a polynomial expression for the area of the cardboard rectangle. Simplify the expression.

Answers

1. _____
2. _____
3. _____
4. _____
5. _____
6. _____
7. _____
8. _____
9. _____
10. _____
11. _____
12. _____
13. _____
14. _____
15. _____
16. _____
17. _____

Name _____ Date _____

Chapter Test B

For use after Chapter 13

In Exercises 18–23, find the product and simplify.

18. $(x + 7)(x + 12)$ **19.** $(m - 6)(m + 8)$

20. $(2n - 1)(n - 8)$ **21.** $(t + 11)(t - 11)$

22. $(4r + 3)(r + 2)$ **23.** $(-y - 8)(2y + 7)$

24. You deposit $200 into a savings account with interest compounded annually. The expression $200(1 + r)^2$, where r is the interest rate, gives the account balance after 2 years. Expand this expression and simplify. Find the account balance if $r = 0.04$.

25. An apple falls from an apple tree that is hanging over a cliff. It hits the ground after 5 seconds. The equation $y = -16t^2 + 15$ gives the apple's height (in feet) in relation to the top of the cliff after t seconds. Write the equation in function notation and find the height of the cliff.

Complete the table of values. Then graph the function.

26. $f(x) = -6x^2$

x	−2	−1	0	1	2
f(x)					

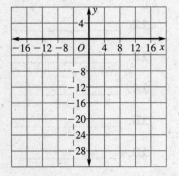

27. $f(x) = 4x^2 - 5$

x	−2	−1	0	1	2
f(x)					

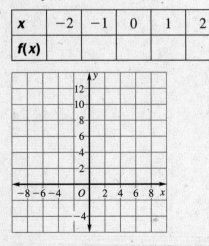

Answers

18. _____

19. _____

20. _____

21. _____

22. _____

23. _____

24. _____

25. _____

_____

26. ___See left.___

27. ___See left.___

Name _____ Date _____

Chapter Test C

For use after Chapter 13

In Exercises 1 and 2, simplify the polynomial and write it in standard form.

1. $11 - 5x^3 + 3x + 9x^3 - 8 + x$ **2.** $5y^2 + 7(3y + 4y^2) - 11y$

3. A boy throws a ball upward at 26 ft/sec. Evaluate the polynomial $-16t^2 + 26t + 4$ to find the ball's height, in feet, after $t = 1.5$ seconds.

In Exercises 4–9, find the sum or difference.

4. $(3x^2 + 7x - 11) + (-8x^2 + 3x - 5)$

5. $(y^3 + 5y + 8) - (7y^3 + 3y^2 + 8)$

6. $(-p^3 + 2p - 7) - (4p^3 + 2p^2 - 1)$

7. $(4n^2 - 9) + (3n + 7) - (n^2 - 6n)$

8. $3(2m^2 - 8m + 1) + 2(4m^2 + 7m)$

9. $-5(q^3 - 2q + 8) - (q - 6) + 8q^3$

10. Write a polynomial expression for the perimeter of the trapezoid. Simplify the polynomial.

$3x + 5$
$2x + 3$
$x + 11$
$2(2x + 3)$

In Exercises 11–16, simplify the expression.

11. $(15y^2)(4xy^3)$ **12.** $(m^5 n^2)^3$ **13.** $3w^2(4w^4 - 7)$

14. $3(-a^2 bc^3)^4$ **15.** $-6r^2(r^2 s^6 t^4)^3$ **16.** $(-4y^3 z)(-2y^2 z^4)^2$

17. A contractor is building a wooden deck around a rectangular pool. The pool is 3 times as long as it is wide. The deck will be 8 feet wide on each side of the pool. Write a polynomial expression for the area of the deck. Simplify the expression.

Answers

1. _____
2. _____
3. _____
4. _____
5. _____
6. _____
7. _____
8. _____
9. _____
10. _____
11. _____
12. _____
13. _____
14. _____
15. _____
16. _____
17. _____

Name _____ Date _____

Chapter Test C

For use after Chapter 13

In Exercises 18–23, find the product and simplify.

18. $(y + 9)(y + 9)$

19. $(-7c - 5)(c - 8)$

20. $(2x - 15)(2x + 15)$

21. $(3a - 7)(4a + 9)$

22. $(12x - 8)\left(\frac{1}{4}x - 3\right)$

23. $(m^3 - 5)(m^3 + 7)$

24. The length of a rectangle is 7 less than 3 times a number x. The width is the number x plus 9. Write and simplify a polynomial expression for the area of the rectangle.

Complete the table of values. Then graph the function.

25. $f(x) = -3x^2 + 4$

x	-2	-1	0	1	2
$f(x)$					

26. $f(x) = 5x^2 - 7$

x	-2	-1	0	1	2
$f(x)$					

Answers

18. _____

19. _____

20. _____

21. _____

22. _____

23. _____

24. _____

25. ___ See left. ___

26. ___ See left. ___

27. _____

_____

28. _____

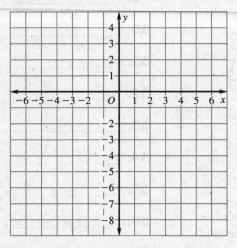

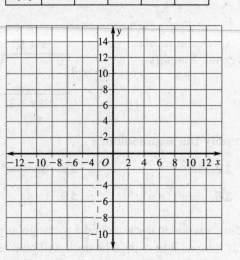

27. An arrow is shot from a bow at an upward angle to reach a distant target. The height of the arrow can be found by using the equation $h = -16t^2 + 25t + 5$, where t is the time in seconds. Write this equation in function notation. Then find the height of the arrow after 1.5 seconds.

28. Write a function in function notation for the values in the table.

x	-2	-1	0	1	2
$f(x)$	18	9	6	9	18

Multiple Choice

1. Simplify the polynomial
   $7(x^2 + 4x^3 - 5) - 4x^2$.
   Write the answer in standard form.

   Ⓐ $28x^3 + 3x^2 - 35$

   Ⓑ $4x^3 + 3x^2 - 5$

   Ⓒ $3x^2 + 4x^3 - 5$

   Ⓓ $3x^2 + 28x^3 - 35$

2. Find the sum
   $(5y^2 + 7y - 8) + (3y^2 - 5y - 4)$.

   Ⓕ $8y^2 + 2y - 4$ Ⓖ $8y^2 + 2y - 12$

   Ⓗ $8y^2 + 12y - 12$ Ⓘ $8y^2 - 2y - 12$

3. Find the difference
   $(-m^2 + 5m + 7) - (3m^2 - 2m + 8)$.

   Ⓐ $-4m^2 + 3m - 1$

   Ⓑ $2m^2 + 3m + 15$

   Ⓒ $-4m^2 + 7m - 1$

   Ⓓ $-4m^2 + 3m + 15$

4. Simplify the expression $(5x^4y)(3x^2y)$.

   Ⓕ $15x^6y$ Ⓖ $8x^6y^2$

   Ⓗ $15x^8y$ Ⓘ $15x^6y^2$

5. Simplify $5y(y - 7) - 3y(y + 2)$.

   Ⓐ $2y^2 - 5y$ Ⓑ $2y^2 - 41y$

   Ⓒ $8y^2 - 18y$ Ⓓ $8y^2 - 5y$

6. Simplify the expression $(-2q^4)^5$.

   Ⓕ $32q^{20}$ Ⓖ $-32q^{20}$

   Ⓗ $32q^9$ Ⓘ $-32q^9$

7. Simplify the expression $3s^2 t (4s^3 t^2)^3$.

   Ⓐ $192s^{11}t^7$ Ⓑ $192s^8t^6$

   Ⓒ $12s^8t^6$ Ⓓ $12s^{11}t^7$

8. Find the product and simplify.
   $(x - 6)(x + 4)$

   Ⓕ $x^2 + 2x - 24$ Ⓖ $x^2 - 2x - 2$

   Ⓗ $x^2 - 2x - 24$ Ⓘ $x^2 + 10x - 24$

9. Which expression shows the correct
   expression for the area of the rectangle?

   Ⓐ $2x^2 + 9x + 18$

   Ⓑ $2x^2 + 18x + 18$

   Ⓒ $2x^2 + 12x + 9$

   Ⓓ $2x^2 + 15x + 18$

   $x + 6$
   $2x + 3$

10. Find the value of the function $f(x) = 2x^2 - 8$
    for $x = -4$.

    Ⓕ 56   Ⓖ 24   Ⓗ -40 Ⓘ 40

Short Response

11. Explain how to find the sum and then
    classify the simplified polynomial.

    $(3x^4 - 7x^3 + 2x^2 - 9) +$
    $(-2x^3 - 2x^2 - 8x + 9)$

Extended Response

12. Graph the functions $f(x) = -x^2 + 9$ and
    $f(x) = x^2 - 9$ using tables of values with
    $x = -3, -2, -1, 0, 1, 2,$ and 3. Describe
    the differences in the graphs.

CHAPTER 13
Alternative Assessment and Math Journal

For use after Chapter 13

Journal

1. In this chapter you learned how to determine if a graph represents a function. Explain this technique. Then sketch an example of a graph that is a function and a graph that is not a function.

Multi-Step Problem

2. You open a business making and selling bookcases. It is determined that the cost for producing x bookcases is given by the function:

$$f(x) = 155 + 48x.$$

Each of the bookcases is sold for $79.

a. Is the expression $155 + 48x$ a *monomial*, *binomial*, or *trinomial*?

b. The *revenue* for selling x bookcases refers to the amount of money earned if x bookcases are sold. The revenue function is given by $f(x) = 79x$. Find the revenue if 21 bookcases are sold.

c. Your *profit* is given by the difference of the revenue and cost functions. Simplify the expression $79x - (155 + 48x)$. Write the profit function.

d. Find the profit you make for selling 21 bookcases.

e. The break-even point occurs when the profit equals zero. How many bookcases need to be produced and sold to reach the break-even point? That is, find the value of x so that the profit function equals zero.

f. Last week you made and sold 80 bookcases. If you make and sell 100 bookcases this week, how much will this week's profit increase over last week's profit?

g. If you know that the cost of producing x tables is $(50x + 75)$ and you wish to produce $(2x + 10)$ of theses tables, there is a total cost of $(50x + 75)(2x + 10)$. Find this product.

h. For the first year, the number of bookcase orders per month can be modeled by the function $f(x) = \dfrac{1}{2}x + 20$ where x is the month of the year. Use a table of values to graph the function.

Name _____ Date _____

Alternative Assessment Rubric
For use after Chapter 13

Journal Solution

1. Complete answers should include the following:

- The technique is called the *vertical line test*. If any vertical line passes through the graph in more than one place, then the graph is not a function.

- Students should sketch one example that passes and one example that does not pass the vertical line test.

Multi-Step Problem Solution

2. a. binomial

b. $1659

c. $31x - 155; f(x) = 31x - 155$

d. $496

e. 5 bookcases

f. $620

g. $100x^2 + 650x + 750$

h. Tables may vary.

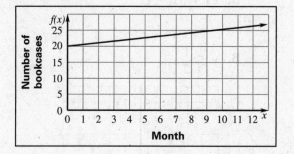

Multi-Step Problem Rubric

4 The student makes one or no computational errors and has a correct graph.

3 The student makes two errors and/or does not have a correct graph.

2 The student makes three or four errors and/or does not have a correct graph.

1 The student makes more than four errors.

Name _____ Date _____

Unit 4 Test
For use after Chapters 11–13

1. Tell whether the relation is a function. Explain your answer.
   (1, 6), (3, 9), (2, 5), (3, 7), (4, 8)

2. Make a scatter plot of the data. Then describe the relationship.

Hours of practice	4	8	12	16
Games won	3	7	13	20

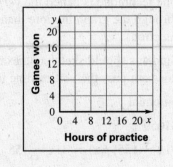

Find the slope of the line passing through the points.

3. (7, −4), (11, −7)

4. (−19, −14), (−15, −12)

Rewrite the equation in slope-intercept form. Then find the slope and y-intercept of the graph of the equation.

5. $y - 6x = 12$

6. $2y + 5x = 12$

Graph the inequality.

7. $y > -3x + 6$

8. $y \le \frac{1}{2}x$

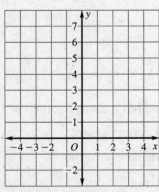

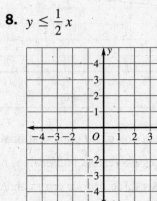

In Exercises 9 and 10, use the data showing the amounts of money spent by 12 people at a store.
$5, $11, $17, $8, $21, $14, $25, $15, $9, $19, $22, $30

9. Make a stem-and-leaf plot of the data.

10. Make a box-and-whisker plot of the data.

Answers

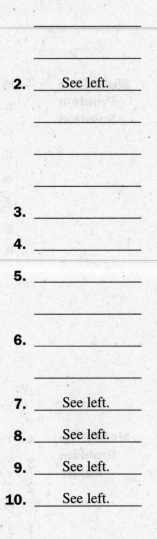

1. _____

   _____

   _____

2. ____See left.____

   _____

   _____

   _____

   _____

3. _____

4. _____

5. _____

   _____

6. _____

   _____

7. ____See left.____

8. ____See left.____

9. ____See left.____

10. ____See left.____

Name _____ Date _____

Unit 4 Test

For use after Chapters 11–13

11. Alys wins 45% of the races she runs in. What are the odds that she will win the next race?

12. Eight friends are going to a movie in two cars. How many different 4-person combinations are possible in the first car?

13. In how many different ways can a president, treasurer, and secretary be appointed from a committee of 5 people?

14. You flip a coin. Then you flip the coin again. Are the two events *independent* or *dependent*?

In Exercises 15 and 16, simplify the polynomial and write it in standard form.

15. $5x^2 + 3x + 9 - 7x + 3x^2 - 4$ **16.** $3(x^2 - 4x + 3) + 2x^2 - 5x$

17. Write polynomial expressions for the perimeter and the area of the rectangle. Simplify the polynomials.

$2x - 7$

$3x + 2$

Simplify the expression.

18. $7m(3m - 6)$ **19.** $(-3q^2 r^5)(13qr^4)$ **20.** $(-2x^3 y^4)^4$

In Exercises 21 and 22, find the sum or difference.

21. $(-7n^2 + 4n + 6) + (3n^2 + 2n)$ **22.** $(8t^3 + 3t - 11) - (6t^2 - 4t + 5)$

23. Complete the table of values. Then graph the function.

$f(x) = -x^2 - 3$

x	−2	−1	0	1	2
f(x)					

Answers

11. _____

12. _____

13. _____

14. _____

15. _____

16. _____

17. _____

_____

18. _____

19. _____

20. _____

21. _____

22. _____

23. _____ See left.

Name _____ Date _____

Cumulative Test
For use after Chapters 1–13

Evaluate the expression.

1. $48 \div [(17 - 11)(8 - 6)]$ **2.** $(7 + 2)^3 \div 3^2$

Solve the equation using mental math.

3. $52 - x = 39$ **4.** $\dfrac{72}{x} = 8$

5. A car is traveling 21 feet per second. How far does it travel in 6 seconds?

Find the sum or difference.

6. $17 + |-12|$ **7.** $8 - (-15)$ **8.** $-52 + (-39)$

Evaluate the expression when $a = 5$, $b = -4$, and $c = -2$.

9. $\dfrac{c - 14}{b}$ **10.** $6b - 7c$ **11.** $\dfrac{ab}{c^2}$

In Exercises 12–15, solve the equation.

12. $x - \dfrac{1}{2} = \dfrac{3}{8}$ **13.** $-5 = \dfrac{m}{-3}$

14. $6a - 11 = 13$ **15.** $2(7y + 8) = 8(y - 1)$

16. Find the height of a triangle with a base of 30 meters and an area of 270 square meters.

Solve the inequality. Then graph its solution.

17. $y + 21 < 13$

<+——+——+——+——+——+——+——+——+>
−10 −9 −8 −7 −6 −5 −4 −3

18. $6x - 19 < x + 6$

<+——+——+——+——+——+——+——+——+>
0   1   2   3   4   5   6   7

Find the greatest common factor and least common multiple.

19. 60, 75, 90   **20.** $25u^6v^4,\ 30u^2v^3$

Complete the statement with <, >, or =.

21. $\dfrac{27}{12}$ —— $\dfrac{13}{6}$ **22.** $-\dfrac{7}{18}$ —— $-\dfrac{4}{9}$

Answers

1. _____
2. _____
3. _____
4. _____
5. _____
6. _____
7. _____
8. _____
9. _____
10. _____
11. _____
12. _____
13. _____
14. _____
15. _____
16. _____
17. _____
See left.
18. _____
See left.
19. _____
20. _____
21. _____
22. _____

Cumulative Test
For use after Chapters 1–13

UNIT 4 Continued

Simplify. Write the expression using only positive exponents.

23. $6^2 a^{-5} \cdot 6^3 a^2$

24. $\dfrac{4^3 m^6 n^{-7}}{4^{-2} m^5 n^2}$

Find the sum, difference, product, or quotient.

25. $-\dfrac{5}{9} + \dfrac{7}{12}$

26. $1\dfrac{4}{5} \cdot 3\dfrac{2}{3}$

27. $8.791 - 11.85$

In Exercises 28–30, solve the equation.

28. $-4.08 + x = 7.5$

29. $-0.35y = 0.56$

30. $\dfrac{3}{8}z = \dfrac{15}{16}$

31. Order the numbers, $\dfrac{19}{4}$, $4\dfrac{3}{5}$, 4.55, $4\dfrac{5}{12}$, and 4.05 from least to greatest.

Find the indicated measurement, where r = radius, d = diameter, and C = circumference. Use 3.14 for π.

32. $r = 5$ in., $C =$ _____

33. $C = 75.36$ m, $d =$ _____

In Exercises 34 and 35, solve the proportion.

34. $\dfrac{24}{36} = \dfrac{14}{x}$

35. $\dfrac{65}{52} = \dfrac{25}{y}$

36. A savings account pays a simple interest rate of 3% per year. How much money should you put in the account to earn $172.50 in 5 years?

In Exercises 37 and 38, write the percent as a decimal and as a fraction.

37. 28%

38. 290%

39. A drawer contains 3 white T-shirts, 4 black T-shirts, and 2 navy blue T-shirts. You randomly select a T-shirt from the drawer. What is the probability that it is navy blue?

Answers

23. _____

24. _____

25. _____

26. _____

27. _____

28. _____

29. _____

30. _____

31. _____

32. _____

33. _____

34. _____

35. _____

36. _____

37. _____

_____

38. _____

_____

39. _____

Name _____ Date _____

Cumulative Test
For use after Chapters 1–13

In Exercises 40 and 41, find the values of x and y.

Answers

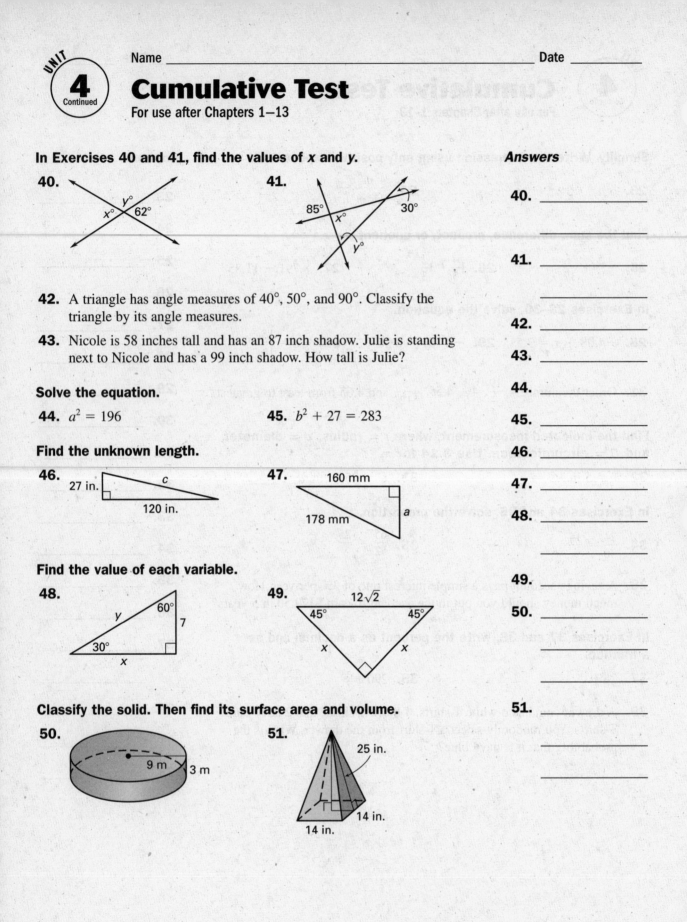

40.

41.

42. A triangle has angle measures of 40°, 50°, and 90°. Classify the triangle by its angle measures.

43. Nicole is 58 inches tall and has an 87 inch shadow. Julie is standing next to Nicole and has a 99 inch shadow. How tall is Julie?

Solve the equation.

44. $a^2 = 196$

45. $b^2 + 27 = 283$

Find the unknown length.

46.

47.

Find the value of each variable.

48.

49.

Classify the solid. Then find its surface area and volume.

50.

51.

40. _____

_____

41. _____

_____

42. _____

43. _____

44. _____

45. _____

46. _____

47. _____

48. _____

_____

49. _____

50. _____

_____

_____

51. _____

_____

_____

Cumulative Test

For use after Chapters 1–13

52. Write a function rule that relates *x* and *y*.

Input *x*	−1	0	1	2
Output *y*	3	1	−1	3

53. Find the slope and *y*-intercept of the graph of the equation $3x + y = 2$. Then graph the equation.

54. Make a stem-and-leaf plot and a box-and-whisker plot of the data.
21.6, 19.8, 20.3, 19.5, 20.7, 18.7, 20.1, 19.9, 21.0, 19.3

Answers

52. _____

53. _____

_____ See left. _____

54. _____ See left. _____

55. _____

56. _____

57. _____

58. _____

59. _____

60. _____

61. _____

62. _____ See left. _____

Find the sum or difference.

55. $(2x^2 − 7x + 11) + (−4x^2 − 2x + 3)$

56. $(−y^2 + 8y − 2) − (3y^2 + 4y − 5)$

Simplify the expression.

57. $(4m^2 n^3)(−3mn^4)$ **58.** $5x(2x^3 − 7)$ **59.** $(−3r^2 t^3)^3$

Find the product and simplify.

60. $(x + 9)(x + 3)$ **61.** $(x − 7)(x + 4)$

62. Complete the table of values for $f(x) = −3x^2 + 5$. Then graph the function.

x	−2	−1	0	1	2
f(x)					

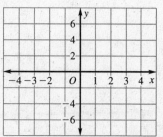

Post-Course Test

For use after Chapter 13

In Exercises 1–3, use the table that shows the number of students that graduated at a high school from 1995–2000.

1. Make a bar graph of the data.

2. How many students graduated after 1997?

3. Predict the number of students that graduated in 2001. Explain your reasoning.

Year	1995	1996	1997	1998	1999	2000
Graduates	210	215	220	224	231	235

Evaluate the expression.

4. $15 + 12 - 6$

5. $\dfrac{(1 + 4)^3}{5}$

6. $17 - 3x$ when $x = 4$

7. $\dfrac{3}{4}y + 1$ when $y = 8$

Find the perimeter and area of the rectangle or square.

8.
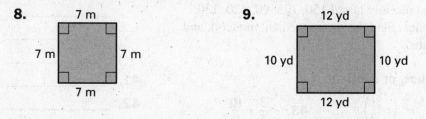

7 m, 7 m, 7 m, 7 m

9. 12 yd, 10 yd, 10 yd, 12 yd

Write the absolute value and the opposite of the integer.

10. 17

11. -24

Find the sum, difference, product, or quotient.

12. $-61 + 18$

13. $-10 + (-22)$

14. $-9 - 72$

15. $-8(15)$

16. $-12(-11)$

17. $-48 \div 8$

Simplify the expression by combining like terms.

18. $7 - 7x + 8x - 1$

19. $12a + 7 + 2b - 3(a + b)$

Solve the equation.

20. $a + 9 = 15$

21. $t - \dfrac{2}{5} = \dfrac{1}{5}$

22. $2.4b = -9.6$

23. $\dfrac{s}{-3} = 1.1$

24. $\dfrac{f}{5} = -8.5$

25. $2d + 8 = 18$

26. $-4c - 1 = -21$

27. $7 - \dfrac{f}{2} = 12$

28. $\dfrac{g}{4} + 5 = 8$

Answers

1. See left.
2. _____
3. _____
   _____
   _____
4. _____
5. _____
6. _____
7. _____
8. _____
   _____
9. _____
   _____
10. _____
11. _____
12. _____
13. _____
14. _____
15. _____
16. _____
17. _____
18. _____
19. _____
20. _____
21. _____
22. _____
23. _____
24. _____
25. _____
26. _____
27. _____
28. _____

Solve the inequality. Then graph its solution.

Answers

29. $\dfrac{x}{4} \geq -2$

30. $-7x + 3 < 24$

29.
See left.

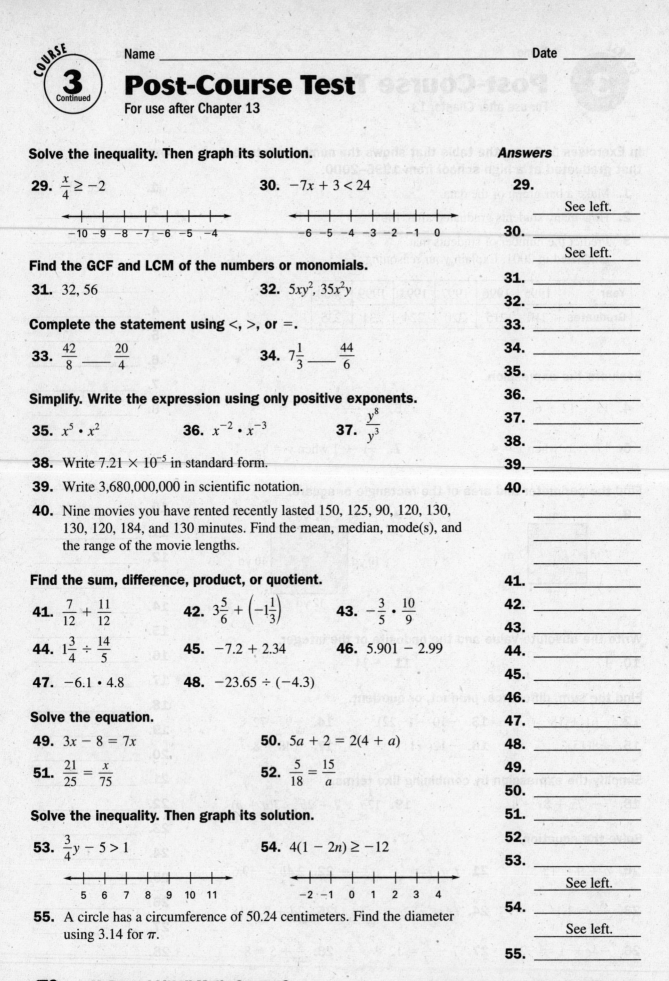

30.
See left.

Find the GCF and LCM of the numbers or monomials.

31. 32, 56

32. $5xy^2,\ 35x^2y$

31. _____

32. _____

Complete the statement using <, >, or =.

33. $\dfrac{42}{8}$ _____ $\dfrac{20}{4}$

34. $7\dfrac{1}{3}$ _____ $\dfrac{44}{6}$

33. _____

34. _____

35. _____

Simplify. Write the expression using only positive exponents.

36. _____

35. $x^5 \cdot x^2$

36. $x^{-2} \cdot x^{-3}$

37. $\dfrac{y^8}{y^3}$

37. _____

38. _____

38. Write 7.21×10^{-5} in standard form.

39. _____

39. Write 3,680,000,000 in scientific notation.

40. _____

40. Nine movies you have rented recently lasted 150, 125, 90, 120, 130, 130, 120, 184, and 130 minutes. Find the mean, median, mode(s), and the range of the movie lengths.

_____

_____

_____

_____

Find the sum, difference, product, or quotient.

41. _____

41. $\dfrac{7}{12} + \dfrac{11}{12}$

42. $3\dfrac{5}{6} + \left(-1\dfrac{1}{3}\right)$

43. $-\dfrac{3}{5} \cdot \dfrac{10}{9}$

42. _____

43. _____

44. $1\dfrac{3}{4} \div \dfrac{14}{5}$

45. $-7.2 + 2.34$

46. $5.901 - 2.99$

44. _____

45. _____

47. $-6.1 \cdot 4.8$

48. $-23.65 \div (-4.3)$

46. _____

47. _____

Solve the equation.

48. _____

49. $3x - 8 = 7x$

50. $5a + 2 = 2(4 + a)$

49. _____

51. $\dfrac{21}{25} = \dfrac{x}{75}$

52. $\dfrac{5}{18} = \dfrac{15}{a}$

50. _____

51. _____

52. _____

Solve the inequality. Then graph its solution.

53. _____

53. $\dfrac{3}{4}y - 5 > 1$

54. $4(1 - 2n) \geq -12$

See left.

54. _____

55. A circle has a circumference of 50.24 centimeters. Find the diameter using 3.14 for π.

See left.

55. _____

Name _____ Date _____

Post-Course Test
For use after Chapter 13

Write the percent as a decimal and as a fraction.

56. 34.5%   **57.** 0.25%

58. You buy a DVD for $8.99 plus 6% sales tax. What is your total cost?

59. A book that has an original price of $15 is discounted 25%. What is the sale price of the book?

60. You randomly pick a marble from a bag that contains 4 yellow, 15 red, 8 blue, and 11 green marbles. What is the probability that you pick a blue marble?

Find the measure(s) of the numbered angle(s).

61.

62.

63. Find the sum of the angle measures in a 14-gon.

64. Draw $\triangle ABC$ in a coordinate plane with the vertices $A(1, 1)$, $B(1, 5)$, and $C(4, 1)$. Dilate $\triangle ABC$ by a scale factor of 3 and label the vertices A', B', C', respectively. Is $\triangle A'B'C'$ similar or congruent to $\triangle ABC$?

65. Find the following square roots:
$\sqrt{4}, \sqrt{49}, -\sqrt{144}$.

66. Order the numbers $\frac{15}{18}$, 0.7, $0.\overline{77}$, $\frac{8}{9}$, and $\sqrt{0.5}$, from least to greatest.

Find the value(s) of the variable(s). Give an exact answer.

67.

68.

69. Write the sine, cosine, and tangent ratios for $\angle D$ in $\triangle DEF$.

Answers

56. _____

57. _____

58. _____

59. _____

60. _____

61. _____

62. _____

63. _____

64. _____

65. _____

_____

66. _____

_____

67. _____

68. _____

69. _____

_____

Find the area of the figure. Use 3.14 for π.

70.

6 ft

71.
16 in.

7 in.

9 in.

72. How many faces, edges, and vertices does a square pyramid have?

Find the surface area and volume of the solid. Use 3.14 for π.

73.
26 cm

4 cm

74.
20 mm

18 mm

30 mm

75. Decide whether the relation $(-8, 16)$, $(8, 16)$, $(16, 8)$, $(-8, -16)$ is a function. Explain your answer.

76. Write a function rule that relates x and y.

Input x	-2	-1	0	1
Output y	4	3	2	1

Tell whether the ordered pair is a solution of the equation.

77. $3x + 2y = 3$; $(1, 0)$

78. $y = -\frac{1}{4}x + 5$; $(1, 5.25)$

Graph the equation. Identify the intercepts and slope of the graph.

79. $-2x + y = 7$

80. $x - 3y = 15$

81. Find the slope of the line passing through the points $(-2, 4)$ and $(0, 8)$.

82. Graph the inequality $y < \frac{1}{2}x + 1$.

Answers

70. _____

71. _____

72. _____

73. _____

_____

74. _____

_____

75. _____

_____

76. _____

77. _____

78. _____

79. ___See left.___

_____

80. ___See left.___

_____

81. _____

82. ___See left.___

Post-Course Test

For use after Chapter 13

In Exercises 83 and 84, use the following depths, in inches, of snowfall for different days: 2, 6, 1, 0, 2, 12, 1, 5, 2, 3, 9, 15.

Answers

83. Make an ordered stem-and-leaf plot of the data. Identify the interval that includes the most data.

83. _____ See left. _____

_____

84. Make a box-and-whisker plot of the data.

84. _____ See left. _____

85. In a survey about favorite colors, 15 students chose blue, 8 chose red, 7 chose purple, 4 chose green, and 16 chose other. Represent the data in a circle graph.

85. _____

86. _____

86. The code to unlock your bicycle lock contains 5 digits. How many different codes are possible?

87. _____

88. _____

In Exercises 87–90, evaluate the expression.

89. _____

87. $_6P_2$ **88.** $_{10}P_1$ **89.** $_5C_3$ **90.** $_7C_5$

90. _____

91. There are 5 starters on a basketball team. In how many different ways can the starters stand in a row?

91. _____

92. A shelf holds 20 DVDs. How many ways can you select 2 DVDs from the shelf?

92. _____

93. You roll a number cube. What are the odds of rolling an even number?

93. _____

Simplify the polynomial and write it in standard form.

94. _____

94. $4 + 4x - x^2 + 7 - x$ **95.** $2(y + 4) - 8y + y^2 - 8$

95. _____

Simplify the expression.

96. _____

96. $(5x^2 + x - 4) + (x^2 - 2x + 9)$ **97.** $(x^3 + x^2 + 6x + 1) - (2x^2 - x + 3)$

97. _____

98. $(-2m^2)(5m^4)$ **99.** $(6xy^3)^2$ **100.** $(3x - 2)(x + 4)$

98. _____

101. Rewrite $y = 3x - 1$ using function notation. Then graph the function using a table of values with $x = -2, -1, 0, 1,$ and 2.

99. _____

100. _____

101. _____

_____ See left. _____

Tell whether the graph represents a function.

102. _____

102.   **103.**

103. _____

Name _____ Date _____

Algebra Readiness Test

For use after Chapter 13

Evaluate the expression when $a = 3.2$, $b = 5$, and $c = -8$.

1. $2a + b$ **2.** $5ab$ **3.** $\dfrac{10a}{b}$

4. $b^2 - a^2$ **5.** $\dfrac{a^2}{b}$ **6.** $c - a$

7. $b - c + a$ **8.** $\dfrac{-16b}{c}$ **9.** $\left(-b^2\right)c$

In Exercises 10–17, write the phrase or sentence as a variable expression or equation. Use x as the variable.

10. A number decrease by 105

11. A number plus 4

12. The quotient of 16 and a number

13. A number is 120% of 16.

14. The product of 15 and a number is 45.

15. Twice the sum of 16 and a number is 20.

16. Three times the quotient of a number and 2 is 6.

17. The quotient of a number and 6 is equal to the number decreased by 4.

Evaluate $y + (-201)$ for the given value of y.

18. $y = 105$ **19.** $y = -316$

20. $y = |-285|$ **21.** $y = -|-400|$

Simplify the expression.

22. $-52 + [y + (-17)]$ **23.** $a + 7b + 3a$ **24.** $-5c + 8 + 5c + 2$

25. $3r + s - (-2r) - 2s$ **26.** $\dfrac{f}{12} - \dfrac{7f}{12}$ **27.** $-\dfrac{b}{6} + \dfrac{5b}{6}$

Evaluate the expression when $x = \dfrac{2}{5}$ and $y = -\dfrac{3}{8}$.

28. $-\dfrac{5}{6}x$ **29.** $2\dfrac{1}{3}y$ **30.** xy

31. $\dfrac{5}{9} \div x$ **32.** $2\dfrac{1}{4} \div y$ **33.** $x \div y$

Answers

1. _____
2. _____
3. _____
4. _____
5. _____
6. _____
7. _____
8. _____
9. _____
10. _____
11. _____
12. _____
13. _____
14. _____
15. _____
16. _____
17. _____
18. _____
19. _____
20. _____
21. _____
22. _____
23. _____
24. _____
25. _____
26. _____
27. _____
28. _____
29. _____
30. _____
31. _____
32. _____
33. _____

Name _____   Date _____

Algebra Readiness Test

For use after Chapter 13

Solve the equation. Write your answer in simplest form.

34. $8 + x = 4$

35. $x + (-2) = 11$

36. $x - 3 = 12$

37. $x - 3.1 = 7.4$

38. $6x = -24$

39. $-11x = 132$

40. $\dfrac{x}{21} = 8$

41. $\dfrac{x}{-1.1} = 9$

42. $5x + 4 = -1$

43. $13 - 2x = -1$

44. $15 + \dfrac{x}{3} = 17$

45. $x - \dfrac{1}{4} = \dfrac{3}{4}$

46. $\dfrac{2}{3} + x = \dfrac{1}{3}$

47. $\dfrac{2}{5} + \dfrac{1}{3} - x = 1\dfrac{1}{15}$

48. $x - \dfrac{2}{7} = \dfrac{1}{4}$

49. $\dfrac{3}{2}a = -1$

50. $\dfrac{4}{5}b = 4\dfrac{4}{5}$

51. $-\dfrac{5}{3}c = -6\dfrac{2}{3}$

52. $1.8 + x = 4.3$

53. $x - 2.5 = -7.1$

54. $9.6 = x - 8.4$

55. $1.7x = -6.29$

56. $\dfrac{x}{-4.5} = -9.2$

57. $\dfrac{x}{1.3} = 4.68$

58. $2y - 5y + 8y = 30$

59. $16z - 11 + 2z + 1 = -1$

60. $-17 = 6x - (1 + 2x)$

61. $\dfrac{3w + 5}{-8} = -4$

62. $8g - 10 = 6g$

63. $2f + 8 = -7f - 10$

64. $3.6d + 1.2 = 8.4(d - 1)$

65. $\dfrac{1}{2}(4\ell + 2) = 3(\ell - 2)$

Solve the equation. Round your answer to the nearest hundredth, if necessary.

66. $36 = \ell^2$

67. $a^2 = 1600$

68. $t^2 + 16 = 137$

69. $m^2 - 5 = 4$

70. $41 = r^2 - 2$

71. $d^2 + 0.2 = 1.24$

72. Evaluate $\sqrt{x^2 + y^2}$ when $x = 12$ and $y = 9$.

73. Evaluate $\sqrt{x^2 - y^2}$ when $x = -17$ and $y = 15$.

Answers

34. _____
35. _____
36. _____
37. _____
38. _____
39. _____
40. _____
41. _____
42. _____
43. _____
44. _____
45. _____
46. _____
47. _____
48. _____
49. _____
50. _____
51. _____
52. _____
53. _____
54. _____
55. _____
56. _____
57. _____
58. _____
59. _____
60. _____
61. _____
62. _____
63. _____
64. _____
65. _____
66. _____
67. _____
68. _____
69. _____
70. _____
71. _____
72. _____
73. _____

Name _____ Date _____

Algebra Readiness Test

For use after Chapter 13

Write a phrase or sentence describing the inequality.

74. $g \leq -2$

75. $9 < a$

76. $2(x + 1) > 6$

77. $\dfrac{r}{-12} \geq 3$

Solve the inequality.

78. $x + 5 > 7$

79. $3x \geq 7$

80. $\dfrac{x}{8} < -10$

81. $\dfrac{x}{-11} + 6 < 4$

82. $8g - 7 > 2g + 11$

83. $-0.3t - 9 + 5.8t \leq -6.25$

Factor the monomial.

84. $16ab$

85. $55x^3y^4$

86. $126fg^3h$

Find the GCF and LCM of the monomials.

87. $9z^4, 15z^7$

88. $14w^2, 42wx$

89. $20ab^3, 200abc^5$

90. $19m^8np, 78m^3p^2$

91. Write the fraction $\dfrac{-16xy}{52x^2}$ in simplest form.

Simplify. Write the expression using only positive exponents.

92. $a^7 \cdot a^4$

93. $\dfrac{g^{11}}{g^3}$

94. $\dfrac{4^3 d^{10} e^3}{4^2 d^{-3} e}$

Find the value of x.

95. $\dfrac{x}{9} = \dfrac{25}{45}$

96. $\dfrac{7}{12} = \dfrac{x}{48}$

97. $\dfrac{81}{36} = \dfrac{9}{x}$

98. $\dfrac{7.3}{2.1} = \dfrac{x}{12.6}$

99. $\dfrac{2x}{3} = \dfrac{60}{15}$

100. $\dfrac{4}{x - 3} = \dfrac{8}{10}$

Answers

74. _____

75. _____

76. _____

77. _____

78. _____

79. _____

80. _____

81. _____

82. _____

83. _____

84. _____

85. _____

86. _____

87. _____

88. _____

89. _____

90. _____

91. _____

92. _____

93. _____

94. _____

95. _____

96. _____

97. _____

98. _____

99. _____

100. _____

Algebra Readiness Test
For use after Chapter 13

In Exercises 101–102, write a function rule that relates *r* and *t*.

101.

Input *r*	−2	0	2	4	6
Output *t*	1	0	−1	−2	−3

102.

Input *r*	−2	−1	0	1	2
Output *t*	5	4	3	2	1

103. Rewrite $4x^2 + y = 16$ using function notation.

Tell whether the ordered pair is a solution of the equation.

104. $2x + 5y = 3;\ \left(1, \dfrac{1}{5}\right)$

105. $y = x - 10;\ (10, 10)$

106. $\dfrac{1}{7}x + y = 0;\ (-7, 1)$

107. $y = 6.7x + 10;\ (-2, 23.4)$

Tell whether the ordered pair is a solution of the inequality.

108. $x > y;\ (8, 8)$

109. $5x + 5y > 20;\ (1, 2)$

110. $2.2x + y > 13;\ (4, -5)$

111. $\dfrac{5}{2}x - 3y \geq \dfrac{3}{2};\ (-2, -2)$

Rewrite the equation in slope-intercept form.

112. $x + 3y = 9$

113. $x - y = 5$

114. $y + 2x = 7$

115. $\dfrac{1}{4}y - 4 = 7$

116. $\dfrac{1}{3}x + \dfrac{2}{3}y = 2$

117. $-x - y + 3 = 0$

Simplify the polynomial and write it in standard form.

118. $6 + x - x^2 + 4 - x$

119. $3(y + 1) - y + y^2$

Simplify the expression.

120. $\left(x^2 + x - 3\right) + \left(4x^2 - 2x + 1\right)$

121. $\left(x^2 + 7x + 2\right) - \left(2x^2 - x + 6\right)$

122. $\left(3n^2\right)\left(-4n^4\right)$

123. $\left(-r^3 t^2\right)^2$

124. $(x + 4)(x + 9)$

125. $(4x - 1)(x + 3)$

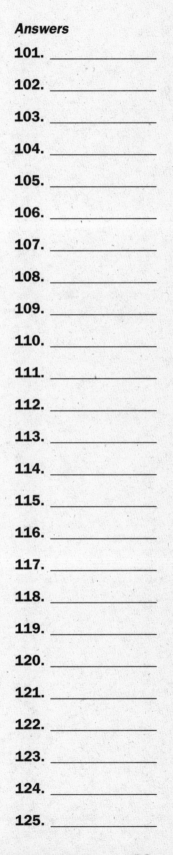

Answers

101. _____

102. _____

103. _____

104. _____

105. _____

106. _____

107. _____

108. _____

109. _____

110. _____

111. _____

112. _____

113. _____

114. _____

115. _____

116. _____

117. _____

118. _____

119. _____

120. _____

121. _____

122. _____

123. _____

124. _____

125. _____

Answers

Pre-Course Test

1. $1 \times 1000 + 1 \times 100 + 9 \times 1$ **2.** $1 \times 1,000,000 + 9 \times 100,000 + 8 \times 10,000 + 6 \times 1000 + 4 \times 100 + 3 \times 10 + 2 \times 1$

3. $5 \times 10 + 6 \times 1 + 1 \times 0.1 + 9 \times 0.01$

4. $2 \times 100 + 8 \times 10 + 6 \times 1 + 3 \times 0.1 + 9 \times 0.01 + 3 \times 0.001$ **5.** 200 **6.** 1490 **7.** 741,000

8. 63,500 **9.** 16.1 **10.** 284 **11.** 758.93 **12.** 0.1

13. 2, 4, and 8 **14.** 2, 3, 4, 6, 8, and 9

15. 2, 4, 5, 8, and 10 **16.** 2, 3, 4, 6, 8, and 9

17. $\frac{8}{3}$ **18.** $\frac{85}{9}$ **19.** $\frac{329}{15}$ **20.** $\frac{196}{11}$ **21.** $2\frac{2}{5}$ **22.** $9\frac{1}{2}$

23. $15\frac{8}{9}$ **24.** $12\frac{6}{13}$ **25.** 6 to 13 **26.** 9 to 15

27. 13 to 17 **28.** 4 to 36 **29.** 12.91 **30.** 6.153

31. 4.72 **32.** 18.148 **33.** $1\frac{4}{7}$ **34.** $\frac{11}{13}$ **35.** $\frac{8}{17}$

36. $\frac{1}{3}$ **37.** 235 tickets **38.** $2.62 **39.** 5 **40.** 4

41. $\frac{5}{13}$ **42.** $\frac{4}{39}$ **43.** 20.8 **44.** 3218.6 **45.** 154.389

46. 4724.566 **47.** 3.4 **48.** 5 **49.** $36\frac{44}{71}$ **50.** $5\frac{397}{500}$

51. 3 batches of cookies **52.** $4.37 **53.** $5.29

54. *Sample Answer:* A, B, E, F

55. *Sample Answer:* $\overrightarrow{AE}$, $\overrightarrow{CF}$, $\overrightarrow{BA}$

56. *Sample Answer:* $\overleftrightarrow{AD}$, $\overleftrightarrow{CF}$

57. *Sample Answer:* $\overline{AB}$, $\overline{AE}$, $\overline{AD}$ **58.** $\angle ABC$, $\angle CBA$, $\angle B$ **59.** $\angle DEF$, $\angle FED$, $\angle E$ **60.** $\angle GHI$, $\angle IHG$, $\angle H$ **61.** $2\frac{7}{8}$ inches **62.** $1\frac{11}{16}$ inches

63. 4.8 centimeters **64.** 2.3 centimeters

65–70. Check drawings. **71.** 134° **72.** 59°

73. 180°

74.

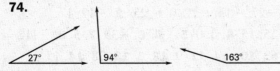

75–78. Check drawings. **79.** 10 hours; *Sample Answer:* A majority of the students study 10 hours each week. **80.** 6 hours; *Sample Answer:* None of the students study 6 hours each week.

81. 17 students **82.** 5 students

83.

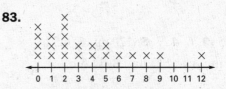

84. about 24 students **85.** literature/fiction; romance **86.** about 12 students

87.

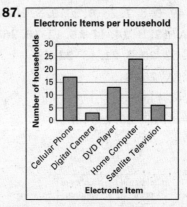

88. *Sample Answer:* The sheep and lamb inventory is decreasing over these years. **89.** greatest change: between 1994 and 1995; least change: between 2000 and 2001

90.

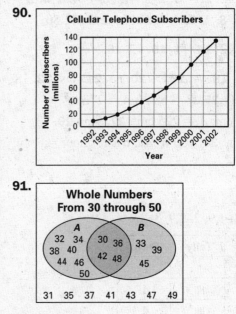

91.

Whole Numbers
From 30 through 50

A: 32 34 38 40 44 46 50
A∩B: 30 36 42 48
B: 33 39 45

31 35 37 41 43 47 49

Chapter 1

Quiz 1

1. spirit club **2.** 23 **3.** no **4.** 41 **5.** 22 **6.** 8

7. 7 **8.** 72 **9.** 59 **10.** 13 **11.** 66 **12.** 101 **13.** 9

Quiz 2

1. 31 **2.** 15 **3.** 6 **4.** 7 **5.** 120 mi **6.** 6.5 h
7. $P = 44$ in.; $A = 117$ in.^{2} **8.** 11.5 h

Test A

1. bar graph **2.** violin **3.** trumpet and sax
4. percussion **5.** 49 **6.** 8 **7.** 26 **8.** 23 **9.** $201
10. C **11.** D **12.** A **13.** B **14.** 34 **15.** 12 **16.** 36
17. 64 **18.** 81 **19.** 52 **20.** 3 **21.** 13 **22.** 22
23. 12 **24.** 63 **25.** A **26.** B
27. $P = 22$ in.; $A = 24$ in.^{2}
28. $P = 36$ m; $A = 81$ m^2 **29.** 255 mi
30.

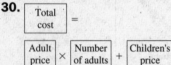

31. $114 **32.** 16 hours

Test B

1. bar graph **2.** 5 **3.** 2–3, 4–5, 6–7 **4.** 4 **5.** 2
6. 39 **7.** 6 **8.** 4 **9.** 367 **10.** 64 **11.** $11.50
12. 60 **13.** 22 **14.** 11 **15.** 12 **16.** $x + \dfrac{3}{8}$
17. $3f + 5s$ **18.** = **19.** > **20.** no **21.** yes **22.** 18
23. 4 **24.** 50 **25.** $P = 68$ m; $A = 273$ m^2
26. $P = 60$ cm; $A = 225$ cm^2 **27.** 9 m **28.** 13
29. 65 ft/min **30.** 180 ft **31.** 6 acres/hour
32. 92 cars

Test C

1. 0–0.9, 1–1.9, 2–2.9, 3–3.9, 4–4.9
2.

Hours	Tally	Freq.
0–0.9	II	2
1–1.9	IIII	4
2–2.9	IIII	4
3–3.9	III	3
4–4.9	II	2

3. Histogram; the data are in equal intervals.

4. The bars in a histogram touch each other at the sides. **5.** 4 **6.** 21.7 **7.** 412 **8.** 9
9. $7 \cdot (9 - 8 + 7) = 56$
10. $64 \div (11 - 3) + 4 = 12$ **11.** 39.9 **12.** 39.6
13. $3s + 5\ell$ **14.** $1.4d + 2.65g - 0.75$; $6.34
15. 1600 **16.** 23 **17.** 58 **18.** 10 **19.** 4
20. $4823 + w = 12{,}760$; 7937 pounds **21.** 8
22. 130 ft^2 **23.** 3.5 ft **24.** 4 in. **25.** $3\frac{1}{3}$ mi
26. $3\frac{1}{2}$ h **27.** 57.5 mi/h **28.** 5 and 16
29. 75 min or $1\frac{1}{4}$ h

Standardized Test

1. C **2.** H **3.** B **4.** G **5.** D **6.** H **7.** A **8.** I
9. B **10.** $6x = 306$; $x = 51$ pages
11.

$$\boxed{\text{Distance}} = \boxed{\substack{\text{Driver 1}\\\text{hours}}} \times \boxed{\substack{\text{Driver 1}\\\text{speed}}} + \left(\boxed{\substack{\text{Driver 2}\\\text{hours}}} - \tfrac{1}{2}\right) \times \boxed{\substack{\text{Driver 2}\\\text{speed}}}$$

465 miles

Alternative Assessment

1. a. Explanations should include these facts:
The bars touch at the sides in a histogram, but not in a bar graph; A histogram is used when the data are grouped in evenly-spaced intervals.
b. A verbal model labels necessary information in a real-world situation.
2. a. perimeter **b.** area **c.** 240 ft^2 **d.** 64 ft
e. 40 ft by 24 ft **f.** 128 ft; twice the perimeter of the flower garden **g.** 960 ft^2; four times the area of the flower garden **h.** The vegetable garden would have twice as much area as the flower garden.

Chapter 2

Quiz 1

1. $-27, -15, -12, 0, 6, 25$ **2.** -17; 17
3. 15; 15 **4.** 0; 0 **5.** -4 **6.** -39 **7.** 5 **8.** -112
9. 63 **10.** -4 **11.** 9 **12.** 3 **13.** 28 **14.** 15
15. 3 **16.** 86 ft; 6 ft

Quiz 2

1. 60; commutative property of addition
2. 22; commutative property of addition, associative property of addition **3.** 160; associative property of multiplication

4. -1600; commutative property of multiplication **5.** $3x + 5y$ **6.** $7x - 4$

7.

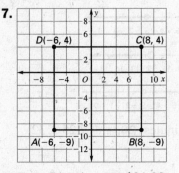

8. *B* **9.** 54 units **10.** $21.90

Test A

1. $-32, -27, -13, 0, 8, 11, 15$ **2.** $-19; 19$

3. $21; 21$ **4.** $1; 1$ **5.** $<$ **6.** $>$ **7.** $<$ **8.** $>$ **9.** -3

10. -12 **11.** 19 **12.** -11 **13.** -9 **14.** -11

15. 20 **16.** -20 **17.** $19 **18.** 78 **19.** -192

20. 7 **21.** 0 **22.** 60 **23.** 2 **24.** -9 **25.** $190

26. *C* **27.** *B* **28.** *A* **29.** *D* **30.** $9(6) + 9(8)$

31. $-6(5) - 6(3)$ **32.** $19x$ **33.** $7a - 3b$

34. $(-2, 3)$ **35.** *D* **36.** Quadrant IV

37. $G(0, -2)$

38–39.

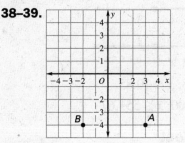

40. 5 units

Test B

1. $>$ **2.** $<$ **3.** $<$ **4.** $>$ **5.** $-30, -27, -16, 17,$ $31, 40$ **6.** 7 **7.** 15 **8.** -8 **9.** -1 **10.** -181

11. -16 **12.** -54 **13.** -143 **14.** 31 **15.** -56

16. -2 **17.** -32 **18.** sometimes **19.** sometimes

20. always **21.** never **22.** 312 **23.** -198 **24.** -8

25. 6 **26.** -2880 **27.** 312 **28.** 10 **29.** -24

30. -2 **31.** 8; associate property of multiplication

32. 21; commutative property of multiplication

33. 6; distributive property

34. 8; commutative property of addition

35. $-45x$ **36.** $4x - 42$ **37.** $-4x + 8y$

38. $8x - 13$ **39.** *D*

40. Quadrant III **41.** $(1, -3)$

42.

43. square **44.** 20 units

Test C

1. $-(-12)$ **2.** $-|15|$ **3.** $-|-5 + (-3)|$ **4.** -201

5. 28 **6.** $-$ **7.** -4 **8.** $-21, -|17|, -|-8|,$ $|-12|, -(-15), |23|$ **9.** -262 **10.** -55 **11.** 81

12. -121 **13.** -285 **14.** 179 **15.** 53 **16.** 36

17. 2 inches below normal **18.** -528 **19.** -630

20. $-\dfrac{2}{3}$ **21.** $\dfrac{5}{12}$ **22.** -5 **23.** 361 **24.** -406

25. $-3a - b - 4$ **26.** $4x + 14y - 21$

27. $3.3x - 13.2y$ **28.** $xy - 21x + 35y$ **29.** $114

30.

31. 20 units **32.** 24 square units

33. $A(-3, 1), B(-5, -4), C(-1, -3)$

Standardized Test

1. B **2.** F **3.** B **4.** H **5.** D **6.** H **7.** D **8.** H

9. A **10.** G **11.** $-$1, or a decrease of $1.

12. $7(36.35 + 24.15)$; distributive property

Alternative Assessment

1. Check student answers: description of like terms, how to add like terms, and using the distributive property to combine like terms.

2. a. The point will be 2 units to the left and

Chapter 2 *continued*

1 unit higher than City Hall. **b.** 4 **c.** 6 **d.** (7, −4) **e.** City Hall **f.** x-coordinate; increase **g.** Add the horizontal and vertical distance for each policeman. Then add those distances together. Divide the sum by 3.

Chapter 3

Quiz 1

1. 38 **2.** −7 **3.** −72 **4.** 11 **5.** $3d = 54$; 18 dogs **6.** $6n = 45$; 7.5 **7.** $5n − 3 = 22$; 5 **8.** $7.90 + 1.25x = 11.65$; 3 toppings

Quiz 2

1. 120 in.^{2}; 46 in. **2.** 8 in. **3.** 12 m **4.** 9 ft

5. $x < 24$;

6. $5 \geq t$;

7. $6 \geq t$;

8. $a > −45$;

9. $x + 2516 > 6700$; $x > 4184$ pounds

10. $0.75x \leq 10$; $x \leq 13$ rides

Test A

1. subtract 7 **2.** divide by −9 **3.** 8 **4.** 32 **5.** 39 **6.** −11 **7.** 64 **8.** −15 **9.** 1 **10.** 7 **11.** −8

12. $5x = 18.75$; $x = 3.75$

13. price + shipping/handling = total cost

14. $23.50 + x = 27.25$ **15.** 3.75 **16.** B **17.** A

18. C **19.** $2.25 **20.** 108 m^2; 54 m **21.** 117 ft^2; 44 ft **22.** 8 m **23.** 9 in. **24.** 12 in. **25.** $x < 11$

26. $12 \geq t$ **27.** $y \leq 4$ **28.** $m > −18$ **29.** $x > 36$

30. $x \leq 15$ **31.** yes **32.** no **33.** yes

34. $21.35 + x \leq 45$; up to $23.65

Test B

1. 68 **2.** −6 **3.** $\frac{3}{9} = \frac{1}{3}$ **4.** −184 **5.** 7 **6.** −4

7. 2 **8.** 255 **9.** 12 **10.** $15 **11.** 423

12. $\frac{6n}{10} = 3$; 5 **13.** $16 + 2n = 52$; 18

14. $4n − 11 = −3$; 2 **15.** $65 + 18x = 209$; 8 people **16.** 143 m^2; 48 m **17.** 33 in.^{2}; 31 in.

18. 17 ft **19.** 16 m **20.** $x > −12$

21. $x \leq 8$

22. $−3 \leq x$;

23. $n > 12$;

24. $m \leq −3$;

25. $6x \leq 45$; 7.5 minutes **26.** $x + 7.25 \leq 32$; up to $24.75

Test C

1. −62 **2.** −5.38 **3.** 2 **4.** −37.2 **5.** −5 **6.** −200 **7.** 4 **8.** −13 **9.** $2.25 **10.** $3058

11. $3n − 7 = −16$; −3 **12.** $18n + (−26) = 19$; 2.5 **13.** $6 + 7 + 5n = −12$; −5

14. $32 + 1.25x = 45.75$; 11 letters

15. $6x + 45 = 168$; 20.5 hours **16.** 14 in. **17.** 6 ft

18. 42 m **19.** 48 m^2

20. $x \leq 8$;

21. $y < −14$;

22. $x \leq −3$;

23. $x \geq −1$;

24. $5x + 3.75 \leq 58$; $x \leq 10.85$

25. $3x + 345 \leq 2000$; $x \leq 551.67$

Standardized Test

1. C **2.** I **3.** B **4.** H **5.** D **6.** F **7.** B **8.** G **9.** A **10.** G **11.** $4.5s = 630$; $s = 140$ mi/h

12. $96x \leq 30(60)$; $x \leq 18.75$; the most runs possible is 18. The total area available is 1800 square feet. Solving for the number of 96 square foot areas in 1800 square feet, you get 18.75. The decimal part, 0.75, does not fulfill the requirement, so 18 full dog runs are possible.

Alternative Assessment

1. Explanations should include: The perimeter of a triangle is the sum of the lengths of the sides of the triangle. The perimeter of the triangle should be given in centimeters. The area of a triangle is the amount of surface the triangle covers. The area of the triangle should be given in square centimeters.

2. a. $x - 30 = 225$; $x = 255$ **b.** $1.5c = 423$; $c = 282$ **c.** $2t - 50 = 130$; $t = 90$ **d.** $p \geq 80$
e. $4w < 200$; $w < 50$ **f.** Between 15 and 20
g. The answer to the one-step equation is a single value such as $x = -20$. The answer to the one-step inequality is a range of values such as $x > -20$.

Unit 1 Test

1. 9 **2.** 15 **3.** 24 **4.** 305 **5.** $\frac{x}{11}$ **6.** $27 - x$
7. 48 **8.** 44 **9.** 15 **10.** 14 **11.** 14 m **12.** 13 ft
13. > **14.** > **15.** < **16.** = **17.** < **18.** < **19.** -25
20. -428 **21.** 47 **22.** -120 **23.** -288 **24.** 13
25. -22 **26.** -182 **27.** 15 **28.** -84 **29.** -42
30. 45 **31.** $8x - 11y$ **32.** $15x + 19$ **33.** $\frac{2}{3}$ **34.** 11
35. $110 + 11x = 176$; 6 years **36.** 42 in.^{2}
37. 22 cm **38.** 17 m **39.** $w \geq 4.5$ **40.** $x < -31$
41. $x < -16$ **42.** $x \geq 6$

Cumulative Test 1

1.
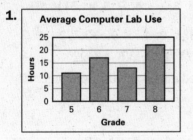
Average Computer Lab Use

2. No **3.** 44 **4.** 11 **5.** 33 **6.** 6 **7.** 464 **8.** 15
9. 4 **10.** 0.5 **11.** $60 + 8y$ **12.** 15 **13.** 86
14. 4 **15.** 11 **16.** $3x = 60$; 20 acorns **17.** 42 in.; 104 in.^{2} **18.** 28 m; 49 m^2 **19.** 429 ft **20.** 1960 mi
21. 512 **22.** 3 **23.** 24 h **24.** -6; -11
25. $-37, -17, -11, 0, 9, 15$
26. $-96, -64, -57, 26, 72$ **27.** 78
28. -52 **29.** -125 **30.** -39 **31.** -48 **32.** 93
33. -357 **34.** 528 **35.** -42 **36.** -18
37. undefined **38.** 12 **39.** $-11x$, $-\$165$
40. -3 **41.** 33; commutative property of addition
42. 4; associative property of addition
43. 14; commutative property of multiplication

44. 2; associative property of multiplication
45. $54 - 63x$ **46.** $66x + 48$ **47.** $-4x + 15$
48. $11x + 9y$ **49.** $(-4, 3)$; Quadrant II
50. $(3, -1)$; Quadrant IV **51.** $(0, -3)$; y-axis
52. $(0, 0)$; origin **53.** -38 **54.** 5.4 **55.** -8
56. -125 **57.** $40.27 = 29 + 0.23x$; 49 min
58. $9t = 252$; \$28 **59.** $7.5h + 92 = 137$; $6h$
60. $2n - 7 = -11$; -2 **61.** $3n - 4 = 14$; 6
62. 44 m^2; 42 m **63.** 8 in. **64.** 16 m **65.** 16 ft
66. $x < 9$ **67.** $x \geq 16$ **68.** $x < -$ **69.** $13 \leq x$
70. $x + 29.85 \leq 45$; up to \$15.15

Chapter 4

Quiz 1

1. $2^3 \cdot 7$ **2.** $2^3 \cdot 5^2$ **3.** $2^2 \cdot 3^2 \cdot 5$ **4.** 12; 72
5. 2; 950 **6.** $9x$; $54x^2yz^2$ **7.** $5xy$; $30x^2y^2$ **8.** Yes
9. Yes **10.** No **11.** 180 seconds

Quiz 2

1. > **2.** = **3.** < **4.** $\frac{8}{5}, 1\frac{11}{18}, 1\frac{11}{15}, 1\frac{7}{9}$
5. $-2\frac{3}{7}, -2\frac{3}{8}, -2\frac{5}{14}, -\frac{9}{4}$ **6.** w^{14} **7.** d^6
8. $\frac{1}{m^3}$ **9.** x^{12} **10.** 8.617×10^6 **11.** 5.716×10^{-7}

Test A

1. 1, 2, 3, 4, 6, 8, 12, 24 **2.** 1, 2, 4, 13, 26, 52
3. $2^3 \cdot 3^2$ **4.** $3 \cdot 5^2$ **5.** 5 **6.** 6 **7.** 60 **8.** 20
9. $\frac{5}{7}$ **10.** $\frac{2}{3}$ **11.** $\frac{9a}{13}$ **12.** Yes **13.** No **14.** 18
15. 120 **16.** 42 **17.** 210 **18.** $12a^2b^2$ **19.** $50x^3y^2$
20. < **21.** = **22.** < **23.** $\frac{1}{6}, \frac{3}{14}, \frac{2}{7}$ **24.** $1\frac{5}{12}, 1\frac{1}{2}, 1\frac{2}{3}$, $1\frac{3}{4}$ **25.** 5^9 **26.** b^{18} **27.** c^4 **28.** $\frac{1}{25}$ **29.** 1
30. $\frac{1}{16}$ **31.** $\frac{1}{a^2}$ **32.** $\frac{1}{b^{10}}$ **33.** 2.14×10^6
34. 1.89×10^{-4} **35.** 0.0000671 **36.** 32,400

Test B

1. 1, 2, 4, 17, 34, 68; composite **2.** 1, 2, 5, 10, 11, 22, 55, 110; composite **3.** 1, 31; prime

4. $2 \cdot 5 \cdot 7$ **5.** $2^3 \cdot 3^2 \cdot 5$ **6.** 12 **7.** 4 **8.** $6xy$

9. 42 **10.** $\dfrac{4}{7}$ **11.** $\dfrac{x}{5y}$ **12.** $\dfrac{-4b^2}{a}$

13. *Sample Answer:* $\dfrac{3}{7}, \dfrac{6}{14}$

14. *Sample Answer:* $\dfrac{10}{18}, \dfrac{20}{36}$ **15.** 180 **16.** 525

17. $42xy^2z^2$ **18.** $30a^2b^2c^3$ **19.** 240 minutes

20. > **21.** = **22.** > **23.** $\dfrac{4}{9}, \dfrac{2}{3}, \dfrac{5}{6}, \dfrac{11}{12}$

24. $-1\dfrac{4}{7}, -1\dfrac{3}{8}, -1\dfrac{1}{3}, -\dfrac{5}{4}$ **25.** m^{17} **26.** n^4

27. 3^2a^3 **28.** $\dfrac{1}{81}$ **29.** $\dfrac{1}{36}$ **30.** 1 **31.** $\dfrac{1}{a}$ **32.** $\dfrac{3}{b^7}$

33. $\dfrac{1}{c^3}$ **34.** 6.2×10^9 **35.** 4.8×10^{14}

36. 3.672×10^{11}

Test C

1. $2^2 \cdot 3 \cdot 5^2$ **2.** $2 \cdot 3^2 \cdot 7^2$ **3.** $3^3 \cdot 5^2 \cdot 7$

4. $5wu$ **5.** $6x^2yz^2$ **6.** $3abc^5$ **7.** $6vu^3$ **8.** 30

9. yes **10.** no **11.** yes **12.** 1260

13. 4725 **14.** $272a^3b^3c^4$ **15.** $180x^5y^2z^4$

16. 1050 seconds **17.** > **18.** < **19.** =

20. $1\dfrac{5}{18}, \dfrac{4}{3}, 1\dfrac{4}{9}, \dfrac{9}{6}$ **21.** $-\dfrac{7}{8}, -\dfrac{5}{6}, -\dfrac{17}{24}, -\dfrac{2}{3}$

22. $3^2x^3y^9$ **23.** $6^5a^8b^{16}c^3$ **24.** $\dfrac{7v}{w^3}$ **25.** 5^9

26. $\dfrac{9}{2x^2}$ **27.** $\dfrac{1}{9a^2b^2}$ **28.** $\dfrac{-2u^4}{v^7}$ **29.** -1 **30.** -4

31. -14 **32.** 1.5982×10^7 **33.** 2.3218×10^{18}

34. 1.6×10^6

Standardized Test

1. B **2.** F **3.** D **4.** H **5.** D **6.** F **7.** B **8.** G

9. D **10.** G **11.** A **12.** 1 row of 32, 2 rows of 16, 4 rows of 8, 8 rows of 4, 16 rows of 2, or 32 rows of 1. 4 rows of 8 or 2 rows of 16 would be better; those arrangements give a better view of the musicians. **13.** 30; work will vary.

Alternative Assessment

1. Complete answers should include:

• Definitions of prime, relatively prime, and composite numbers.

• A method for computing greatest common factor.

2. a. 6,370,000 **b.** 0.0000000000667 **c.** g, f, r

d. $e = \dfrac{fr^2}{g}$ **e.** 5.96×10^{24} kg **f.** $d = \dfrac{e}{v}$

g. 5.37×10^{-3} kg/cm^3 **h.** 0.00537 kg/cm^3 **i.** You would convert the mass to grams by multiplying it by $\dfrac{1000 \text{ g}}{1 \text{ kg}}$. This would give 5.96×10^{27} grams.

Chapter 5

Quiz 1

1. $\dfrac{2}{7}$ **2.** $2\dfrac{1}{4}$ **3.** $\dfrac{11x}{15}$ **4.** $1\dfrac{11}{20}$ **5.** $\dfrac{3x}{4}$ **6.** $2\dfrac{7}{15}$

7. $2\dfrac{3}{4}$ lb **8.** $\dfrac{9}{32}$ **9.** $-1\dfrac{1}{3}$ **10.** 16 **11.** $1\dfrac{1}{2}$

12. $1\dfrac{11}{16}$ **13.** $-\dfrac{2}{5}$ **14.** $2\dfrac{2}{5}$ in.

Quiz 2

1. 0.375 **2.** $0.8\overline{3}$ **3.** $\dfrac{16}{25}$ **4.** $\dfrac{2}{3}$ **5.** 41.311

6. 5.92 **7.** 12.883 **8.** 4.75 **9.** -2.772

10. 2.496 **11.** 2.75 **12.** -3.6 **13.** 22

14. mean: 33; median: 34; mode: 36; range: 12

Test A

1. $1\dfrac{3}{13}$ **2.** $\dfrac{1}{8}$ **3.** $\dfrac{2c}{3}$ **4.** $\dfrac{1}{2}$ **5.** $-5\dfrac{1}{8}$ **6.** $\dfrac{13}{15}$

7. $\boxed{\text{Miles hiked on day 1}} + \boxed{\text{Miles hiked on day 2}} + \boxed{\text{Miles hiked on day 3}} = \boxed{30}$

8. $8\dfrac{2}{3} + 11\dfrac{3}{5} + x = 30$ **9.** $9\dfrac{11}{15}$ mi **10.** $\dfrac{1}{2}$

11. $-\dfrac{2}{21}$ **12.** $17\dfrac{3}{5}$ **13.** $-1\dfrac{1}{15}$ **14.** $\dfrac{4}{15}$ **15.** $1\dfrac{1}{5}$

16. $4\dfrac{3}{8}$ in. **17.** 0.125 **18.** $0.\overline{6}$ **19.** 3.25

20. $-\dfrac{4}{25}$ **21.** $-5\dfrac{1}{20}$ **22.** $\dfrac{5}{11}$ **23.** 3.09, $3\dfrac{1}{5}$, 3.21, $3\dfrac{1}{4}$

24. 7.59 **25.** 11.79 **26.** 1.9 **27.** 7.58 **28.** 3.8

29. -1.24 **30.** \$16 **31.** 9.88 **32.** -4.896

33. -4.2 **34.** 2.6 **35.** 39.1 gal **36.** mean: 3; median: 5; mode: 7; range: 12

Test B

1. $1\frac{13}{19}$ 2. $\frac{1}{2}$ 3. $1\frac{4}{15}$ 4. $\frac{1}{8}$ 5. $-6\frac{1}{12}$ 6. $\frac{11}{14}$

7. $\frac{8a}{15}$ 8. $-\frac{4b}{21}$ 9. $-\frac{c}{3}$ 10. $5\frac{5}{16}$ h 11. $\frac{15}{56}$

12. $2\frac{14}{15}$ 13. $-4\frac{2}{3}$ 14. $\frac{7}{9}$ 15. $-\frac{7}{20}$ 16. $3\frac{1}{33}$

17. 68 mi 18. 5 19. $-1\frac{19}{21}$ 20. 0.64 21. $0.0\overline{6}$

22. 7.3125 23. $3\frac{19}{20}$ 24. $\frac{8}{9}$ 25. $\frac{3}{8}$ 26. $5\frac{1}{4}$, 5.26, $5\frac{4}{15}$, $5\frac{2}{7}$, 5.3 27. -5.539 28. -16.091 29. 7.293

30. -0.95 31. $2.75 32. 11.81 33. -3.1

34. 9.72 35. 2.3 36. 71.5 mi/h 37. mean: 39; median: 40; modes: 38 and 41; range: 10

Test C

1. $-\frac{11}{18}$ 2. $2\frac{5}{16}$ 3. $2\frac{1}{4}$ 4. $-2\frac{13}{20}$ 5. $\frac{x}{6}$

6. $-\frac{11p}{15q}$ 7. $\frac{29a}{42b}$ 8. $\frac{17n}{18}$ 9. $\frac{2}{7}$ 10. $1\frac{1}{10}$

11. $3\frac{19}{36}$ 12. $6\frac{23}{30}$ 13. $\frac{4}{27}$ 14. $-\frac{1}{36}$ 15. $-5\frac{1}{4}$

16. $-1\frac{3}{5}$ 17. $7\frac{1}{2}$ 18. $\frac{11}{36}$ 19. 40 days 20. $0.8\overline{1}$

21. $3.4\overline{6}$ 22. 0.09375 23. $-2\frac{16}{25}$ 24. $\frac{13}{250}$ 25. $\frac{1}{33}$

26. rock, country, pop, jazz, classical 27. 26.13
28. -0.956 29. 0.46748 30. 3.8 31. 15
32. 0.56 33. 28 34. square; 0.33 ft^2
35. 97; median: 93; range: 8

Standardized Test

1. A 2. H 3. D 4. G 5. C 6. F 7. D 8. G

9. C 10. G 11. w = amount of water per

minute, $5w = 8$, $w = \frac{8}{5} = 1\frac{3}{5}$ gal/min;

$17 \cdot 1\frac{3}{5} = 27\frac{1}{5}$, $\frac{27\frac{1}{5} \text{ gal}}{17 \text{ min}}$ 12. mean: 60; median:

58; modes: 55 and 61; range: 28; The median represents the weights fairly well. The value 81 grams is an outlier and causes the mean to be a little high. The modes are too close to the upper and lower ends of the data.

Alternative Assessment

1. Complete answers should include:
- A description of the technique to add/subtract fractions.
- A description of the technique to multiply/divide fractions.
- A statement that you do need a common denominator to add or subtract fractions, but you do not need a common denominator to multiply or divide fractions.

2. a. $1\frac{3}{8}, 1\frac{3}{4}, 1\frac{3}{4}, 1\frac{3}{4}, 2\frac{1}{8}, 2\frac{1}{4}, 2\frac{1}{4}, 3\frac{1}{8}$ b. $1\frac{3}{4}$ h

c. In order from least to greatest: 1.375, 1.75, 1.75, 1.75, 2.125, 2.25, 2.25, 3.125 d. 2.047 h
e. 1.9375 h f. 1.75 h g. 3.5 h h. The Jones family is paying \$.16 less per hour.

Chapter 6

Quiz 1

1. 10 2. -3.5 3. 28 4. 5 5. 5.6 6. $4\frac{1}{14}$

7. 109.5 m 8. 3 adults, 3 children

Quiz 2

1. 28 cm 2. 9 in. 3. $x < 6$ 4. $x \le -3$

5. $y > -8$ 6. $4.2 \le y$ 7. $9n - 6 \ge 66$; $n \ge 8$

8. $3(n + 7) \le 15$; $n \le -2$ 9. $2\frac{1}{2}$ cups

Test A

1. $3m, -11m$ 2. 15, -2 3. -3 4. 13 5. 5
6. -6 7. 100; 1.5 8. 5; -1 9. 12; 24
10. 10; 7.5 11. $120 + 6.25x = 380$
12. 41.6 hours 13. 84 ft 14. 7.5 in. 15. 44 m
16. 50.24 cm 17. 35 ft

18. $x \le 3$

19. $y > 2$

20. $m < 3$

21. $z < 4\frac{1}{2}$

22. $x + 7 \le 21$ 23. $2x < 15$ 24. $52 + 4.75x$
25. $52 + 4.75x \le 75$ 26. $x \le 4.84$; because you cannot buy part of a lure, round your answer down to 4.

Test B

1. 2 **2.** 3 **3.** 3 **4.** 9 **5.** 6 **6.** $8\frac{3}{4}$ **7.** $2\frac{2}{3}$ **8.** 7.2

9. 75 in. **10.** 2668 books **11.** \$.95 **12.** $2\frac{1}{2}$ m

13. 75.36 in. **14.** 94.2 ft

15. $a > -3$

16. $-9 \geq b$

17. $\frac{11}{12} > c$

18. $d \leq 6$

19. $1 \leq e$

20. $f < 68.9$

21. $7(8 - n) > 28$; $n < 4$ **22.** $3n - 6 \leq 15$; $n \leq 7$

23. more than $83\frac{1}{3}$ hours

Test C

1. -2.5 **2.** $-10\frac{1}{3}$ **3.** 9 **4.** 3 **5.** $-\frac{8}{9}$ **6.** -1.8

7. 4 **8.** 49 min **9.** 90 mm **10.** \$1.50

11. $10\frac{1}{2}$ ft **12.** 18.055 mm **13.** $9\frac{31}{56}$ in. **14.** 3 in.

15. $e \geq -3$

16. $k < -1.3$

17. $m < 2\frac{1}{2}$

18. $2 \geq p$

19. $8(15 - n) \geq 70$; $n \leq 6.25$

20. $x + 9 > 3(4 - x)$; $x > \frac{3}{4}$

21. $4x - 15 \leq 2x + 11$; $x \leq 13$

22. $35x > 72 + 18x$; membership costs less for more than 4 terms of classes.

Standardized Test

1. B **2.** H **3.** A **4.** I **5.** B **6.** F **7.** D **8.** F

9. C **10.** $x + (x + 2) + (x + 4) + (x + 6) = 108$; 24, 26, 28, and 30 **11.** $257 + 14x + 21x \leq 370$; $x \leq 3.22857\ldots$; you can buy at most 3 of each movie type.

Alternative Assessment

1. $x \geq 28$; Answers may vary. **2. a.** 3 inches
b. 9.42 inches **c.** 18.84 inches **d.** $2\pi r = 4.375$
e. 0.6966 inches **f.** 5 units **g.** $9 \leq 2\pi r \leq 11$
h. 1.43 inches $\leq r \leq 1.75$ inches

Chapter 7

Quiz 1

1. $\frac{2}{1}$; 2 : 1; 2 to 1 **2.** $\frac{5}{4}$; 5 : 4; 5 to 4

3. 32 mi/gal **4.** 10 **5.** 49 **6.** 15 **7.** 20%

8. 52.5 **9.** 60 **10.** 37.5% **11.** 2.5%

12. 96.8% **13.** > **14.** =

Quiz 2

1. increase, 60% **2.** 102 **3.** 27 **4.** \$178.08

5. 130% **6.** 250 **7.** \$1250 **8.** $\frac{9}{25}$ **9.** $\frac{4}{5}$

Test A

1. $\frac{2}{3}$; 2 : 3; 2 to 3 **2.** $\frac{5}{2}$; 5 : 2; 5 to 2 **3.** yes

4. no **5.** 2200 feet per minute **6.** yes **7.** no

8. 12 **9.** 9 **10.** 12 ft **11.** 24% **12.** 220

13. 21 **14.** 3% **15.** 125% **16.** 40%

17. 0.08; $\frac{2}{25}$ **18.** 1.3; $1\frac{3}{10}$, or $\frac{13}{10}$

19. increase, 28% **20.** decrease, 4% **21.** 92

22. 138.6 **23.** \$100 **24.** \$17.85 **25.** \$16.80

26. \$450 **27.** $\frac{1}{4}$ **28.** $\frac{1}{6}$

Test B

1. $\frac{2}{5}$; 2 : 5; 2 to 5 **2.** $-\frac{1}{2}$; $-1 : 2$; -1 to 2

3. 3600 **4.** \$1.88 **5.** \$.60 per jar **6.** 35 **7.** 7

8. 13.2 **9.** \$19.50 **10.** 127.5 km **11.** 15%

12. 660 **13.** 0.06; $\frac{3}{50}$ **14.** 3.1; $3\frac{1}{10}$ or $\frac{31}{10}$

15. 0.005; $\frac{1}{200}$ **16.** 2.5% **17.** 103.75%

18. 2135.2 **19.** 256.5 **20.** 6% decrease **21.** \$27

22. \$50.70 **23.** $\frac{3}{8}$ **24.** $\frac{1}{2}$ **25.** $\frac{7}{8}$ **26.** 28

Test C

1. 62 words per minute **2.** $.30 per pound
3. 34 **4.** 35 **5.** 48 **6.** 15,000 **7.** 27 **8.** 38
9. $12\frac{1}{2}$ ft **10.** 106 **11.** 35% **12.** $\frac{11}{32}, \frac{3}{8}, 0.38,$
39%, 0.4 **13.** < **14.** > **15.** 150% increase
16. 75% decrease **17.** $29.1\overline{6}$% **18.** $8795.78
19. $39.69 **20.** $3000 **21.** $\frac{7}{50}$ **22.** $\frac{33}{50}$
23. theoretical

Standardized Test

1. D **2.** G **3.** C **4.** G **5.** A **6.** H **7.** B **8.** I
9. C **10.** $46.20; Find the sale price then find the tax on the sale price and add it to the sale price.
11. 2000–2001: 7.5% decrease; $P = \dfrac{3120 - 2886}{3120}$,

2001–2002: 15.0% increase; $P = \dfrac{3320 - 2886}{2886}$,

2000–2002: 6.4% increase; $P = \dfrac{3320 - 3120}{3120}$

Alternative Assessment

1. Complete answers should include:
• Find the percent of data within each category. Multiply the decimal form of each percent by 360. Then draw wedges in the circle whose angles measure the numbers of degrees that you have calculated.
• The sum of the fractions for each of the categories should be 1.
• Examples will vary.

2. a. 1.6 g/1 ml **b.** $\frac{8}{5} = \frac{12}{x}$, where x is the

amount of acid in milliliters **c.** 7.5 ml **d.** 148.75 mg

e. 14.3% **f.** $\frac{19}{25}$ **g.** $\frac{3}{16}$ **h.** Multiply the number of days Jamie works in the lab, 47, by the probability of her getting faulty equipment on any one day, $\frac{3}{16}$. Because $47 \times \frac{3}{16} \approx 8.8$, she probably will get faulty equipment on 8 or 9 days.

Unit 2 Test

1. $7^2 \cdot 3$ **2.** $2^4 \cdot 7$ **3.** 5; 3220 **4.** $6a^3b^4$; $72a^5b^7$
5. < **6.** > **7.** 9^{12} **8.** 17^5 **9.** $\dfrac{3^7 x^2}{y^5}$ **10.** $5^2 a^{11}$
11. 2.08×10^6 **12.** $-\frac{1}{2}$ **13.** $2\frac{7}{11}$ **14.** $5\frac{2}{3}$ **15.** $\frac{1}{9}$
16. $16\frac{2}{3}$ **17.** $\frac{9}{16}$ **18.** $\frac{15}{16}$ min **19.** 4.431
20. -0.772 **21.** 6.25 **22.** 0.000497 **23.** -0.92
24. 10 **25.** $0.5\overline{3}$ **26.** $\frac{1}{25}$ **27.** $\frac{4}{11}$ **28.** $2.10
29. 15 cm **30.** 110 ft **31.** $k \geq -4$ **32.** $s > 8.5$
33. 3 **34.** 7200 beats **35.** 12 servings **36.** 300
37. $0.42, \frac{21}{50}$ **38.** $2.1, 2\frac{1}{10}$ or $\frac{21}{10}$ **39.** $303.60
40. $\frac{4}{11}$ **41.** $\frac{7}{11}$

Cumulative Test

1. 17 **2.** 51 **3.** 23 **4.** 17 **5.** 135 **6.** 4.5 **7.** 50 m;
136 m^2 **8.** 4325 **9.** $-21, -17, -15, -11, -4,$
6, 9 **10.** -34 **11.** -8 **12.** -2 **13.** $35x + 17x$;
$1092 **14.** -4 **15.** -22 **16.** 8 **17.** Check student drawing; 24 units **18.** -64 **19.** -18
20. $75 + 5.25x = 185.25$; 21 **21.** 48 m^2
22. $x < -21$; **23.** $y \geq 3$;

24. 42; 252 **25.** $7mn^2$; $105m^5n^4$ **26.** $-\frac{5}{7}$ **27.** $\frac{3}{2x}$
28. 50 lb: $\frac{2}{5}$; 40 lb: $\frac{3}{8}$; the 50 pound bag **29.** m^8
30. $\dfrac{8^8}{x^6}$ **31.** $\dfrac{2b^6}{a^4}$ **32.** 2.1×10^{-13} **33.** $1\frac{5}{12}$
34. $-2\frac{1}{3}$ **35.** $\frac{2}{3}$ **36.** $9\frac{1}{4}$ **37.** $37\frac{1}{3}$ ft^2 **38.** 4.52
39. 57.34 **40.** 6.8 **41.** 0.577 **42.** $10
43. 109.375 ft^2; 875 bricks **44.** mean: $4.\overline{7}$;
median: 5; mode: 6 **45.** -25 **46.** -2 **47.** 345.4 ft
48. $15 + 6n \geq 27$; $n \geq 2$ **49.** $8n < 2n - 21$;
$n < -3.5$ **50.** 37 trees per acre **51.** $5.25 per hour **52.** 21 **53.** 45 **54.** 27% **55.** 60
56. 1.25% **57.** 8% **58.** $30 **59.** $\frac{1}{3}$ **60.** $\frac{1}{5}$

Chapter 8

Quiz 1

1. neither **2.** complementary **3.** 62°

4. equilateral **5.** isosceles **6.** scalene **7.** 45

8. 57 **9.** 105 **10.** 76

Quiz 2

1. SAS; $2x - 1 = 5$; 3 m **2.** SSS; $5x = 25$; 5

3. 4 **4.** 1 **5.** rotation **6.** reflection in the x-axis

7. translation **8.** reflection in the y-axis

9. 20 ft

Test A

1. supplementary **2.** complementary **3.** 65°

4. $m\angle 2 = 105°$; $m\angle 3 = 75°$ **5.** isosceles

6. scalene **7.** 19; obtuse **8.** square **9.** rhombus

10. 112 **11.** 720° **12.** 1980° **13.** $\angle G \cong \angle M$;

$\angle H \cong \angle N$; $\angle I \cong \angle Q$; $\angle J \cong \angle P$ **14.** 115° **15.** 76°

16. 5 cm **17.** yes **18.** no **19.** rotation

20. translation **21.** $\triangle ABC$, $\triangle GFE$ **22.** $4\frac{1}{2}$ ft

Test B

1. 145° **2.** 50° **3.** 48° **4.** 138° **5.** 42° **6.** $\angle 2$

7. equilateral **8.** scalene **9.** 72°; acute

10. parallelogram **11.** rectangle **12.** hexagon

13. 86 **14.** 145 **15.** 98° **16.** 55° **17.** 11 cm

18. 9 cm

19. 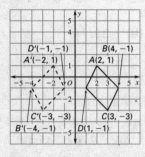 **20.**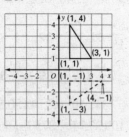

21. 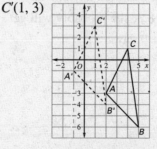 **22.** 67.5 ft

23.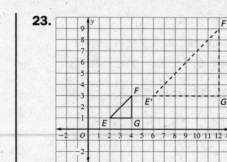

Test C

1. 33°; 123° **2.** 58° **3.** 32° **4.** 90° **5.** 32°

6. 58° **7.** 12; 36° **8.** yes; obtuse **9.** yes; acute

10. $x = 25$; $m\angle A = 35°$, $m\angle C = 55°$

11. $x = 13$; $m\angle D = 56°$, $m\angle E = 60°$,

$m\angle F = 64°$ **12.** $x = 48$; $m\angle B = 127°$,

$m\angle C = 108°$ **13.** $x = 63$; $m\angle H = m\angle I = 126°$,

$m\angle F = 75°$, $m\angle G = 174°$

14. ASA; 23 **15.** SAS; 3

16. $H(-2, 0)$, $I(-4, 2)$, $J(-1, 4)$

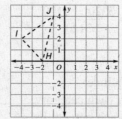

17. $R'(-3, 8)$, $S'(0, 5)$, $T'(-1, 1)$, $U'(-4, 0)$

18. $A'(4, 3)$, $B'(0, 2)$, $C'(-5, 2)$ **19.** $5\frac{5}{8}$ ft

20.

Standardized Test

1. D **2.** G **3.** A **4.** G **5.** A **6.** G **7.** B **8.** I

9. B **10.** SAS **11.** $A'(-1, -1)$, $B'(2, -4)$,

$C'(1, 3)$

Alternative Assessment

1. Complete answers should include:
- A *trapezoid* is a quadrilateral with exactly one pair of parallel sides.
- A *parallelogram* is a quadrilateral with both pairs of opposite sides parallel.
- A *rhombus* is a parallelogram with four sides of equal length.
- A *rectangle* is a parallelogram with four right angles.
- A *square* is a parallelogram with four sides of equal length and four right angles.

2. a. $A(11, 8)$, $B(11, 4)$ **b.** right triangle **c.** all of them **d.** the garage **e.** no lines of symmetry **f.** (18, 24), (33, 24), (33, 39) **g.** reflection in the *x*-axis **h.** The *x*-coordinates for each point would be the same as they were before the reflection; however, the *y*-coordinates would be the opposites of those before the reflection.

Chapter 9

Quiz 1

1. 11 **2.** -10 **3.** 13 **4.** ± 25 **5.** ± 9

6. $=$

$$\sqrt{\frac{9}{16}} = \frac{3}{4}$$

0.2 0.4 0.6 0.8 1.0

7. $>$

$-\sqrt{18}$ -4

-4.4 -4.2 -4.0 -3.8 -3.6

8. 4.9 **9.** 11.7 **10.** 8.1 feet **11.** yes **12.** no

Quiz 2

1. $x = 3$ ft; $y = 3\sqrt{2}$ ft

2. $x = 15$ cm; $y = 15\sqrt{3}$ cm **3.** $x = 5$ in.

4. $x = 7$ m; $y = 14$ m

5. $\sin A = \dfrac{12}{13}$, $\cos A = \dfrac{5}{13}$, $\tan A = \dfrac{12}{5}$;

$\sin B = \dfrac{5}{13}$, $\cos B = \dfrac{12}{13}$, $\tan B = \dfrac{5}{12}$

6. $\sin A = \dfrac{8}{17}$, $\cos A = \dfrac{15}{17}$, $\tan A = \dfrac{8}{15}$;

$\sin B = \dfrac{15}{17}$, $\cos B = \dfrac{8}{17}$, $\tan B = \dfrac{15}{8}$ **7.** 4.121 cm

8. 5.216 in.

Test A

1. ± 6 **2.** ± 20 **3.** 5.7 **4.** -8.1 **5.** ± 13 **6.** ± 8

7. 18 ft **8.** rational; The decimal form repeats.

9. irrational; The decimal form is nonrepeating and nonterminating. **10.** rational; The decimal form terminates.

11. $=$

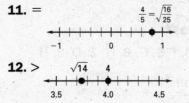

$\dfrac{4}{5} = \sqrt{\dfrac{16}{25}}$

-1 0   1

12. $>$

$\sqrt{14}$ 4

3.5   4.0   4.5

13. 25 **14.** 30 **15.** 60 m **16.** yes **17.** no

18. 20 ft **19.** 34 ft **20.** $11\sqrt{2}$ cm **21.** $\sin L = \dfrac{21}{29}$

22. $\cos L = \dfrac{20}{29}$ **23.** $\tan L = \dfrac{21}{20}$

24. 43.857 mm

Test B

1. 8 **2.** 11 **3.** ± 1 **4.** ± 11 **5.** ± 6 **6.** ± 60

7. $<$

6    $\sqrt{40}$

5.5   6.0   6.5

8. $=$

$\dfrac{2}{3} = \sqrt{\dfrac{8}{18}}$

-1 0   1

9. $\sqrt{10}$, $\dfrac{17}{5}$, $\sqrt{12}$, 3.5 **10.** 16 m **11.** 16.3 in.

12. no **13.** yes **14.** 6.6 ft **15.** 80 cm; 240 cm^2

16. 120 in.; 600 in.^{2} **17.** $x = 6$ m, $y = 6\sqrt{2}$ m

18. $x = 5\sqrt{3}$ in., $y = 10$ in. **19.** $x = 7.5\sqrt{3}$ ft,

$y = 7.5$ ft **20.** $x = 7$ cm **21.** $\sin K = \dfrac{24}{25}$,

$\cos K = \dfrac{7}{25}$, $\tan K = \dfrac{24}{7}$ **22.** $\sin L = \dfrac{7}{25}$,

$\cos L = \dfrac{24}{25}$, $\tan L = \dfrac{7}{24}$ **23.** 19.491 cm

24. 21.751 mm

Test C

1. -16 **2.** $\dfrac{6}{11}$ **3.** ± 7 **4.** ± 9.80 **5.** ± 1.73

6. ± 14.07 **7.** ± 1.6 **8.** 60 ft **9.** 0; rational

10. $\sqrt{32}$; irrational **11.** $-\sqrt{15}$, -3.6, $-\sqrt{\dfrac{16}{9}}$, $-\dfrac{5}{4}$

12. 7.5 **13.** 8.2 **14.** yes

15. 11 m; $A = 52.8$ m^2; $P = 35.2$ m **16.** 20.8 ft

17. $x = 24\sqrt{2}$ cm **18.** $x = 3\sqrt{3}$ mm, $y = 6$ mm

19. $x = 5.5$ ft, $y = 5.5\sqrt{3}$ ft **20.** $x = \dfrac{9}{\sqrt{2}}$

21. 70.7 in. **22.** $\sin(49.68°) = \dfrac{a}{17}$;

$\tan(49.68°) = \dfrac{a}{11}$; 12.96 ft

Standardized Test

1. B **2.** H **3.** C **4.** I **5.** C **6.** H **7.** D **8.** H

9. 277.3 mi **10.** $\sin 31° = \dfrac{\text{opposite}}{\text{hypotenuse}}$;

$\sin 31° = \dfrac{x}{54}$; $0.5150 \approx \dfrac{x}{54}$; 27.81 cm $\approx x$

Alternative Assessment

1. Complete answers should include:
- Correct explanation of the Pythagorean theorem
- Recognition that the Pythagorean theorem applies to right triangles only.

- Explanation of the converse of the Pythagorean theorem
- Example showing a correct use of the converse of the Pythagorean theorem

2. a. 30° **b.** 75.0 ft **c.** 86.6 ft **d.** $\tan A = \dfrac{h}{d}$
e. 35.4 ft **f.** 48.4 ft **g.** We only knew the length of one of the sides of the triangle. To apply the Pythagorean theorem, we would need to know lengths of two of the sides to solve for the third.
h. about 384 m

Chapter 10

Quiz 1

1. 32 in.^{2} **2.** 33 cm^2

3. **4.**

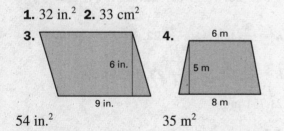

54 in.^{2} 35 m^2

5. 452.16 m^2 **6.** 254.34 yd^2 **7.** 84.9056 cm^2

8. 15 cm **9.** cylinder; not a polyhedron

10. pentagonal prism; polyhedron; faces: 7; edges: 15; vertices: 10

Quiz 2

1. $S = 230$ m^2; $V = 150$ m^3 **2.** $S = 276$ cm^2;
$V = 168$ cm^3 **3.** $S = 753.6$ in.^{2}; $V = 1582.6$ in.^{3}

4. $S = 301.4$ cm^2; $V = 301.4$ cm^3

Test A

1. $A = \dfrac{1}{2}bh$ **2.** $A = \pi^2$ **3.** $A = bh$

4. $A = \dfrac{1}{2}(b_1 + b_2)h$ **5.** 180 cm^2 **6.** 44 ft^2

7. 108 m^2 **8.** 153.86 mm^2 **9.** 4 ft **10.** 13 m

11. sphere; no **12.** rectangular prism; yes

13. Check drawings; faces: 5; edges: 9; vertices: 6

14. 439.6 in.^{2} **15.** 2136 m^2 **16.** 395.64 in.^{2}

17. 452.16 in.^{2} **18.** 84 m^3 **19.** 1256 in.^{3}

20. 192 yd^3 **21.** 414.48 mm^3

Test B

1. 234 cm^2 **2.** 18 mm^2 **3.** 63 yd^2

4. 346.185 m^2 **5.** 15 m **6.** 6 in. **7.** 15 m

8. cone; no **9.** pentagonal pyramid; yes

10. Check drawings; faces: 7; edges: 12; vertices: 7 **11.** 1340 ft^2 **12.** 3768 m^2

13. 593.46 in.^{2} **14.** 95 in.^{2} **15.** hat box

16. 45 in.^{3} **17.** 3391.2 cm^3 **18.** 420 m^3

19. 1004.8 ft^3 **20.** 28.26 ft^3

Test C

1. 91.5 m^2 **2.** 100 in.^{2} **3.** 77.04 cm^2

4. 24.96 ft^2 **5.** 1.7 cm **6.** 13 ft **7.** hexagonal prism; faces: 8; edges: 18; vertices: 12 **8.** cone; not a polyhedron

9.

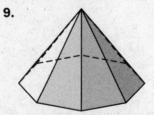

10. 4040 ft^2; 9090 tiles **11.** $S = 406.63$ in.^{2};
$V = 576.975$ in.^{3} **12.** $S = 1000$ ft^2; $V = 1320$ ft^3

13. $S = 3077.2$ m^2; $V = 8792$ m^3

14. $S = 454$ cm^2; $V = 564$ cm^3 **15.** 15 m

Chapter 10 continued

16.

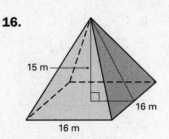

15 m, 16 m, 16 m

17. 17 m; 800 m²

Standardized Test

1. A **2.** G **3.** D **4.** F **5.** C **6.** H **7.** D **8.** G **9.** D

10.

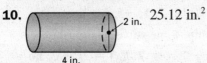

2 in., 4 in., 25.12 in.²

11. $S = 96$ cm²; $V = 64$ cm³; $S_2 = 384$ cm²;

$V_2 = 512$ cm³; $\frac{1}{4}; \frac{1}{8}$

Alternative Assessment

1. Complete answers should include:

• Explanation in words for how to find areas of parallelograms, trapezoids, and circles

• Drawing, algebraic formula for area, and example for each type of figure

2. a. 5 **b.** 9 **c.** 6 **d.** 84 ft³ **e.** 136 ft²

f.

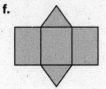

g. about 167 cm³ **h.** 1884 cm³ **i.** 1004.8 cm²

j. The tent is a *solid* because it is a three-dimensional figure that encloses a part of space. The tent is a *polyhedron* because it is enclosed by polygons. The tent is a *prism* because the front and back are congruent triangles in parallel planes and the other faces are rectangles.

Unit 3 Test

1. $m\angle 1 = 32°$; $m\angle 2 = 58°$; $m\angle 3 = 122°$

2. $m\angle 1 = 37°$; $m\angle 2 = 105°$

3. equilateral triangle **4.** rhombus

5. regular hexagon **6.** 2340°

7. $\angle A \cong \angle M$; $\angle B \cong \angle N$; $\angle C \cong \angle Q$; $\angle D \cong \angle P$

8. $\overline{AB} \cong \overline{MN}$; $\overline{BC} \cong \overline{NQ}$; $\overline{CD} \cong \overline{QP}$; $\overline{AD} \cong \overline{MP}$

9. yes **10.** no **11.** ± 9 **12.** ± 13

13. rational; terminating **14.** irrational; nonrepeating and nonterminating **15.** rational; repeating **16.** 41 in. **17.** 36 cm **18.** $5\sqrt{2}$ m

19. 6 ft, $6\sqrt{3}$ ft **20.** 344 in. or 28 ft 8 in.

21. 18 mm² **22.** 16.5 ft² **23.** 200.96 m²

24. pentagonal pyramid; faces: 6; edges: 10; vertices: 6 **25.** $S = 336$ in.²; $V = 288$ in.³

26. $S = 1413$ m²; $V = 3391.2$ m³

Cumulative Test

1. 41 **2.** 10 **3.** $4x + 3y$; \$31.75 **4.** 14 in.

5. -4 **6.** 55 **7.** -210 **8.** 13 **9.** $-6x + 21y$

10. $8x + 15$ **11.** 42 **12.** -279

13. $35x - 515 = 1200$; 49 people

14. $x < 123$ ┄┄┼┄┄○┄┄┼┄┄┼┄┄ 122 123 124 125

15. $x \leq -7$ ┄┼┄┼┄┼┄●┄┼┄┼┄┼┄┼┄┼┄ $-10 -9 -8 -7 -6 -5 -4 -3 -2$

16. 17 ft **17.** 2; 360 **18.** $15a^5b^6$; $90a^7b^9$ **19.** $\frac{11}{15}$

20. 2 m **21.** $\frac{5}{8}, \frac{2}{3}, \frac{5}{7}, \frac{11}{14}$ **22.** x^{15} **23.** $\frac{1}{b^9}$ **24.** $\frac{4n^4}{m^3}$

25. $3\frac{7}{9}$ **26.** $2\frac{1}{12}$ **27.** $-1\frac{1}{3}$ **28.** $\frac{2}{15}$ **29.** $7\frac{1}{2}$ **30.** 13

31. 23.8 **32.** 8.8 **33.** -10.899 **34.** $1.3\overline{8}$ **35.** $\frac{8}{99}$

36. $2\frac{1}{25}$ **37.** 14 cm **38.** $11 + 3x \geq 5x - 9$; $10 \geq x$

39. 1136 mi **40.** 28.8 **41.** 185% **42.** \$47.25

43. $21.\overline{21}\%$ increase **44.** isosceles **45.** equilateral

46. $128\frac{4}{7}°$ **47.** $3x + 8 = 5x - 12$; 10

48. $4x + 7 = 21$; 3.5 **49.** -23.71 **50.** 35.57

51. $\sqrt{\frac{8}{5}}, 1.3, \frac{4}{3}, \sqrt{2}$ **52.** yes

53. 90 mm; $P = 240$ mm; $A = 2160$ mm²

54. $\sin M = \frac{8}{17}$; $\cos M = \frac{15}{17}$; $\tan M = \frac{8}{15}$;

$\sin N = \frac{15}{17}$; $\cos N = \frac{8}{17}$; $\tan N = \frac{15}{8}$

55. 51 in.² **56.** 113.04 m²

57. $S = 268$ ft²; $V = 264$ ft³

Chapter 11

Quiz 1

1. not a function **2.** function **3.** $y = -3x$

4.

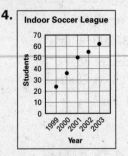

positive relationship; The numbers increased each year.

5. *Sample Answer*: $(0, -5)$, $(1, -1)$, $(2, 3)$

6. *Sample Answer*: $(0, 2)$, $(2, 3)$, $(4, 4)$

7.

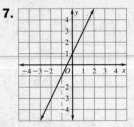

Quiz 2

1. x-intercept: $\frac{1}{2}$, y-intercept: -2

2. x-intercept: 6, y-intercept: 4 **3.** -2 **4.** $\frac{6}{5}$

5. slope: 1; y-intercept: -3

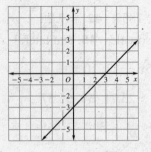

6. slope: $-\frac{3}{5}$; y-intercept: 3

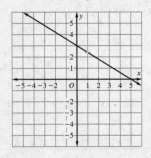

7.

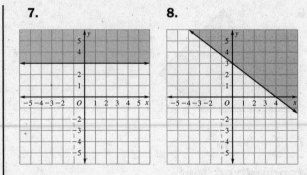

8.

Test A

1. yes **2.** yes **3.** 13; 7; 1; -5

4. no relationship **5.** negative relationship

6. $f(x) = -4x + 7$; yes **7.** $f(x) = 2x + 3$; no

8.

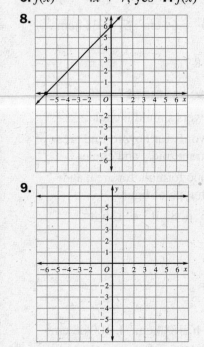

9.

10. x-intercept: 4; y-intercept: 3

11. x-intercept: -2; y-intercept: 3 **12.** negative

13. $\frac{5}{2}$ **14.** $y = -3x - 1$ **15.** $y = 4x - 5$

16. slope: 2; y-intercept: -7

17. slope: -3; y-intercept: 8

18. no **19.** yes **20.** yes

21.

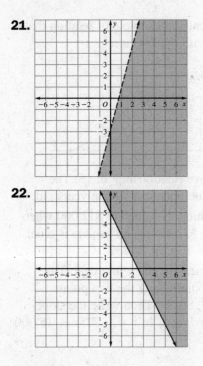

22.

Test B

1. Yes; each input has exactly one output.

2. $y = -2x$ **3.** $y = 3x + 1$

4. Positive relationship; the price of heating oil has increased with time.

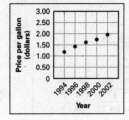

5. no **6.** yes **7.** yes

8.

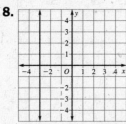

9.

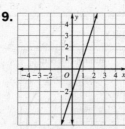

10. *y*-intercept: -6; *x*-intercept: none

11. *y*-intercept: 9; *x*-intercept: -3 **12.** $\frac{10}{7}$ **13.** -2

14. slope: -2; *y*-intercept: 5

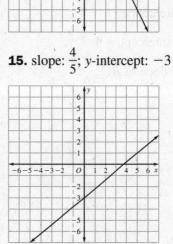

15. slope: $\frac{4}{5}$; *y*-intercept: -3

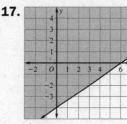

16. yes

17.

18.

19. $\frac{3}{5}$ **20.** 2 **21.** $y = 2x + 6$ **22.** No; *Sample*

Answer: The slope through points *A* and *B* is

$-\frac{1}{5}$ and the slope through points *B* and *C* is -1.

Because the two pairs of points lie on lines with different slopes, the points are not all on the same line.

Test C

1. $y = -2x + 1$ **2.** $y = \frac{2}{3}x - 2$

3. No; for each number of papers delivered (input), there are different amounts of money he could earn (output). **4.** negative **5.** positive

6. yes **7.** no **8.** yes

Chapter 11 *continued*

9. 26 sec

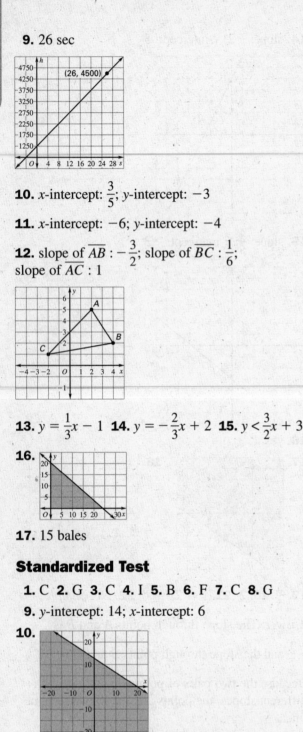

10. x-intercept: $\frac{3}{5}$; y-intercept: -3

11. x-intercept: -6; y-intercept: -4

12. slope of $\overline{AB}$: $-\frac{3}{2}$; slope of $\overline{BC}$: $\frac{1}{6}$; slope of $\overline{AC}$: 1

13. $y = \frac{1}{3}x - 1$ **14.** $y = -\frac{2}{3}x + 2$ **15.** $y < \frac{3}{2}x + 3$

16.

17. 15 bales

Standardized Test

1. C **2.** G **3.** C **4.** I **5.** B **6.** F **7.** C **8.** G

9. y-intercept: 14; x-intercept: 6

10.

Find the largest whole number value of y on the graph where $x = 14$. They can buy at most 3 videos.

Alternative Assessment

1. Complete answers should include:
Explanations of relation, function, domain, range; real-life example of function with domain and range specified; real-life example of relation that is not a function with explanation

2. a.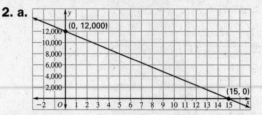

b. -800 **c.** negative relationship **d.** 15; The vehicle has no value once it is fifteen years old.

e. 12,000; The vehicle is valued at $12,000 when it is brand new. **f.** $7200 **g.** The vehicle is older than 7.5 years ($x > 7.5$). **h.** $8832

i. The $15,000 represents the y-intercept. The slope can be computed using the two points $(0, 15{,}000)$ and $(9, 8025)$. Then write the slope-intercept form, $y = mx + b$; $y = -775x + 15{,}000$

Chapter 12

Quiz 1

1. January   February

```
      9 | 0 |
      7 1 | 1 | 1 5 6
    8 8 4 | 2 | 1 2 4 7 9
  6 2 1 0 | 3 | 4 9
```

Key: $2 \mid 4 = 24$ inches; 28 and 23

2.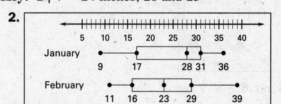

January

3.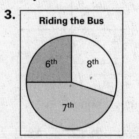

The circle graph is the better choice because it displays the data as parts of a whole.

Quiz 2

1.

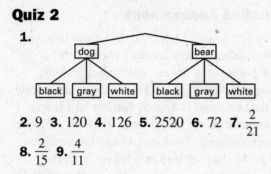

2. 9 **3.** 120 **4.** 126 **5.** 2520 **6.** 72 **7.** $\frac{2}{21}$

8. $\frac{2}{15}$ **9.** $\frac{4}{11}$

Test A

1. 7 | 6; stem: 7; leaf: 6 **2.** 12 | 1; stem: 12; leaf: 1 **3.** 15 | 1; stem: 15; leaf: 1 **4.** lightest: 38 lbs, heaviest: 62 lbs; median weight: 49 lbs

5.
```
1 | 7 9
2 | 2 4 6 7 8
3 | 1 6          Key:  2 | 2 = 22 in.
```

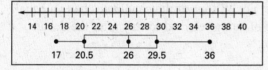

6. 144° **7.** 240° **8.** 162°

9.

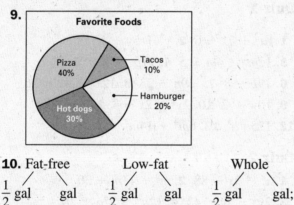

10. Fat-free   Low-fat   Whole

$\frac{1}{2}$ gal ⟍ gal $\frac{1}{2}$ gal ⟍ gal $\frac{1}{2}$ gal ⟍ gal;

6 choices

11. 24 **12.** 120 **13.** 35 **14.** 24 **15.** 10 **16.** 38%

17. $\frac{5}{8}$ **18.** $\frac{6}{19}$ **19.** $\frac{1}{24}$; independent

20. $\frac{1}{22}$; dependent

Test B

1.
```
3 | 6 9
4 | 1 5 7
5 | 2 6
6 | 5
7 | 3          Key:  5 | 2 = 52
```
Interval with the most data: 40–49

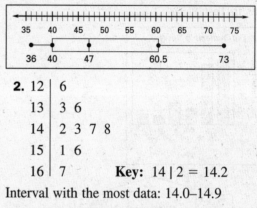

2.
```
12 | 6
13 | 3 6
14 | 2 3 7 8
15 | 1 6
16 | 7          Key:  14 | 2 = 14.2
```
Interval with the most data: 14.0–14.9

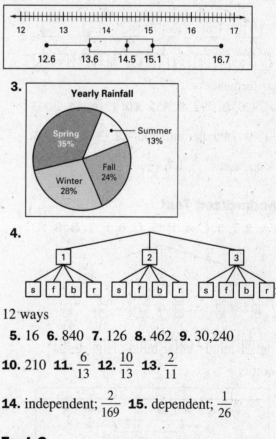

3.

4.

s f b r s f b r s f b r;

12 ways

5. 16 **6.** 840 **7.** 126 **8.** 462 **9.** 30,240

10. 210 **11.** $\frac{6}{13}$ **12.** $\frac{10}{13}$ **13.** $\frac{2}{11}$

14. independent; $\frac{2}{169}$ **15.** dependent; $\frac{1}{26}$

Test C

1. See student stem-and-leaf plots. **2.** 85.5; 88

3.

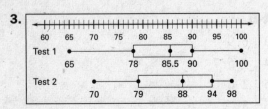

Test 1: 65 — 78 — 85.5 90 — 100

Test 2: 70 — 79 — 88 — 94 98

4. *Sample Answer*: Test 2 has a higher median, and the range of the grades for the middle 50% is higher than that of Test 1. There is a greater range of scores in Test 1.

5.

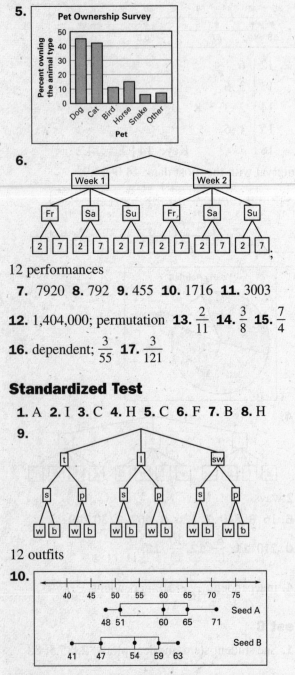

6.

12 performances

7. 7920 **8.** 792 **9.** 455 **10.** 1716 **11.** 3003

12. 1,404,000; permutation **13.** $\frac{2}{11}$ **14.** $\frac{3}{8}$ **15.** $\frac{7}{4}$

16. dependent; $\frac{3}{55}$ **17.** $\frac{3}{121}$

Standardized Test

1. A **2.** I **3.** C **4.** H **5.** C **6.** F **7.** B **8.** H

9.

12 outfits

10.

Seed A: 48 51 — 60 65 — 71

Seed B: 41 47 — 54 59 63

Seed A is growing at a faster rate than seed B.

Alternative Assessment

1. *Sample Answer*: Order the data from largest value to smallest value. Identify each of the extreme values (the lowest and highest values). Next compute the median. This is the middle point of the data (if there is an odd number of values) or the average of the two middle numbers (if there is an even number of values). Using the median to divide the data set into two halves, find the quartiles. The lower quartile is the median of the lower half of the data. The upper quartile is the median of the upper half of the data. Then construct the box-and-whisker plot using these values.

2. a. 720 **b.** $\frac{1}{2}$ **c.** 24 **d.** 1 to 23 **e.** $\frac{1}{16}$

f. 15 **g.** Dependent; knowing that the first topic is the fall dance affects the likelihood that the second topic will be the end of the year party. **h.** Biased sample; not all four of the candidates had an equal chance of being selected to stay after the debate to help.

Chapter 13
Quiz 1

1. $8x^2 + 7x - 6$ **2.** $y^2 + 5y - 15$
3. $12m^2 - 4m + 5$ **4.** $11p^2 + 17p$ **5.** 51
6. $19b - 8$ **7.** $-9n + 23$ **8.** $12x^2 - 4x - 26$
9. $10w - 2$ **10.** $2x^2 + 2x + 3$ **11.** $-18x^5$
12. $125a^3b^3$ **13.** $6m^4 + 14m^2$

Quiz 2

1. $x^2 - 3x - 88$ **2.** $m^2 + 11m + 30$
3. $2y^2 - 5y - 42$ **4.** $12a^2 - 37a + 28$
5. $f(x) = 7x - 11$ **6.** $f(x) = 6x^2 - 4x + 9$
7. $(-2, -8), (-1, -2), (0, 0), (1, -2), (2, -8)$

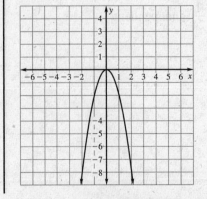

8. $(-2, -3)$, $(-1, -6)$, $(0, -7)$, $(1, -6)$, $(2, -3)$

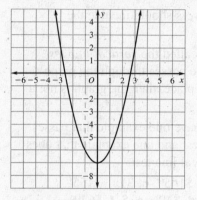

9. yes **10.** no

Test A

1. binomial **2.** trinomial **3.** monomial

4. $-n^2 + 6n + 7$ **5.** $11w^3 + w^2 + 3w - 6$

6. $11x - 9$ **7.** $-7m^2 + 8m + 12$ **8.** $8m + 12$

9. $16a + 18$ **10.** $-3w + 14$ **11.** $3y^2 + 9y - 7$

12. $9x^3 - 12x + 10$ **13.** $4y^2 - 14y + 4$

14. $9x + 3$ **15.** $12q^5$ **16.** $32x^5$ **17.** m^{30}

18. $-125k^3$ **19.** $81a^8$ **20.** $5z^4 - 35z$

21. $5y^2 + 40y$ **22.** $21m^2 - 28m$ **23.** $-18b^2 + 63b$

24. $x^2 + 13x + 22$ **25.** $r^2 - 6r - 16$

26. $t^2 - 10t + 24$ **27.** $f(x) = 7x - 2$

28. $f(x) = -6x^3$ **29.** yes **30.** no

31.

x	−2	−1	0	1	2
f(x)	8	2	0	2	8

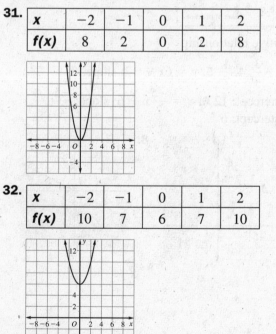

32.

x	−2	−1	0	1	2
f(x)	10	7	6	7	10

Test B

1. $11x^2 - 2x$ **2.** $5y^2 + 9y + 8$ **3.** 53

4. $10x - 12$ **5.** $4q^2 - 8q + 20$ **6.** $3m^2 + 7m + 4$

7. $8n^3 + 2n^2 + 18$ **8.** $-3x^5 - 7x + 8$

9. $x^4 + 2x^2 - 1$ **10.** $6y^2$ **11.** $21x^7$ **12.** $3q^{12}$

13. $45y^2 - 40y$ **14.** $625z^4$ **15.** $-8w^3v^3$

16. $54n^9$ **17.** $3x^2 + 16x + 16$ **18.** $x^2 + 19x + 84$

19. $m^2 + 2m - 48$ **20.** $2n^2 - 17n + 8$ **21.** $t^2 - 121$

22. $4r^2 + 11r + 6$ **23.** $-2y^2 - 23y - 56$

24. $200 + 400r + 200r^2$; 216.32

25. $f(x) = -16x^2 + 15$; 385 ft

26.

x	−2	−1	0	1	2
f(x)	−24	−6	0	−6	−24

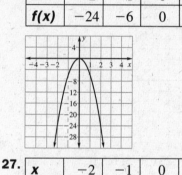

27.

x	−2	−1	0	1	2
f(x)	11	−1	−5	−1	11

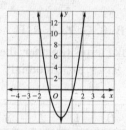

Test C

1. $4x^3 + 4x + 3$ **2.** $33y^2 + 10y$ **3.** 7 feet

4. $-5x^2 + 10x - 16$ **5.** $-6y^3 - 3y^2 + 5y$

6. $-5p^3 - 2p^2 + 2p - 6$ **7.** $3n^2 + 9n - 2$

8. $14m^2 - 10m + 3$ **9.** $3q^3 + 9q - 34$

10. $10x + 25$ **11.** $60xy^5$ **12.** $m^{15}n^6$

13. $12w^6 - 21w^2$ **14.** $3a^8b^4c^{12}$ **15.** $-6r^8s^{18}t^{12}$

16. $-16y^7z^9$ **17.** $64x + 256$ **18.** $y^2 + 18y + 81$

19. $-7c^2 + 51c + 40$ **20.** $4x^2 - 225$

21. $12a^2 - a - 63$ **22.** $3x^2 - 38x + 24$

23. $m^6 + 2m^3 - 35$ **24.** $3x^2 + 20x - 63$

25.

x	−2	−1	0	1	2
f(x)	−8	1	4	1	−8

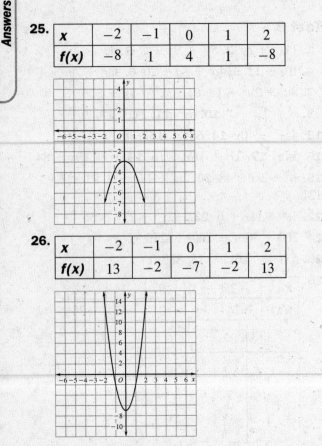

26.

x	−2	−1	0	1	2
f(x)	13	−2	−7	−2	13

27. $f(x) = -16x^2 + 25x + 5$; 6.5 ft

28. $f(x) = 3x^2 + 6$

Standardized Test

1. A **2.** G **3.** C **4.** I **5.** B **6.** G **7.** A **8.** H

9. D **10.** G **11.** Group like terms together, then combine like terms; $3x^4 - 9x^3 - 8x$; trinomial

12. $f(x) = -x^2 + 9$

x	−3	−2	−1	0	1	2	3
f(x)	0	5	8	9	8	5	0

$f(x) = x^2 - 9$

x	−3	−2	−1	0	1	2	3
f(x)	0	−5	−8	−9	−8	−5	0

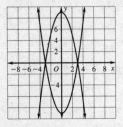

One graph is a reflection of the other in the *x*-axis.

Alternative Assessment

1. Complete answers should include the following:

• The technique is called the *vertical line test*. If any vertical line passes through the graph in more than one place, then the graph is not a function.

• Students should have one example that passes the vertical line test and one example that does not pass the vertical line test.

2. a. binomial **b.** $1659 **c.** $31x - 155$; $f(x) = 31x - 155$ **d.** $496 **e.** 5 **f.** $620

g. $100x^2 + 650x + 750$

h.

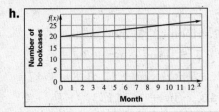

Unit 4 Test

1. No; there are two outputs for the input 3.

2.

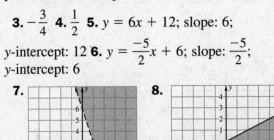

positive relationship

3. $-\dfrac{3}{4}$ **4.** $\dfrac{1}{2}$ **5.** $y = 6x + 12$; slope: 6; *y*-intercept: 12 **6.** $y = \dfrac{-5}{2}x + 6$; slope: $\dfrac{-5}{2}$; *y*-intercept: 6

7.

8.

Unit 4 *continued*

9.

0	5 8 9
1	1 4 5 7 9
2	1 2 5
3	0

Key: 1 | 1 = $11

10.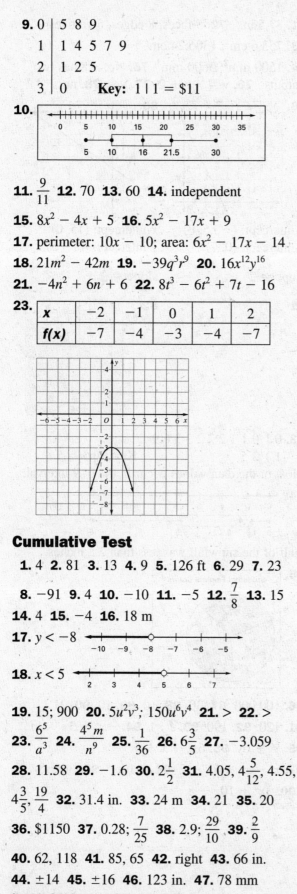

11. $\dfrac{9}{11}$ **12.** 70 **13.** 60 **14.** independent

15. $8x^2 - 4x + 5$ **16.** $5x^2 - 17x + 9$

17. perimeter: $10x - 10$; area: $6x^2 - 17x - 14$

18. $21m^2 - 42m$ **19.** $-39q^3r^9$ **20.** $16x^{12}y^{16}$

21. $-4n^2 + 6n + 6$ **22.** $8t^3 - 6t^2 + 7t - 16$

23.

x	−2	−1	0	1	2
f(x)	−7	−4	−3	−4	−7

Cumulative Test

1. 4 **2.** 81 **3.** 13 **4.** 9 **5.** 126 ft **6.** 29 **7.** 23

8. −91 **9.** 4 **10.** −10 **11.** −5 **12.** $\dfrac{7}{8}$ **13.** 15

14. 4 **15.** −4 **16.** 18 m

17. $y < -8$

18. $x < 5$

19. 15; 900 **20.** $5u^2v^3$; $150u^6v^4$ **21.** > **22.** >

23. $\dfrac{6^5}{a^3}$ **24.** $\dfrac{4^5 m}{n^9}$ **25.** $\dfrac{1}{36}$ **26.** $6\dfrac{3}{5}$ **27.** −3.059

28. 11.58 **29.** −1.6 **30.** $2\dfrac{1}{2}$ **31.** 4.05, $4\dfrac{5}{12}$, 4.55,

$4\dfrac{3}{5}$, $\dfrac{19}{4}$ **32.** 31.4 in. **33.** 24 m **34.** 21 **35.** 20

36. $1150 **37.** 0.28; $\dfrac{7}{25}$ **38.** 2.9; $\dfrac{29}{10}$ **39.** $\dfrac{2}{9}$

40. 62, 118 **41.** 85, 65 **42.** right **43.** 66 in.

44. ±14 **45.** ±16 **46.** 123 in. **47.** 78 mm

48. $x = 7\sqrt{3}$, $y = 14$ **49.** $x = 12$

50. cylinder; $S = 678.24$ m^2; $V = 763.02$ m^3

51. square pyramid; $S = 896$ in.^{2}; $V = 1568$ in.^{3}

52. $y = -2x + 1$

53. slope: −3; y-intercept: 2

54.

18	7
19	3 5 8 9
20	1 3 7
21	0 6

Key: 19 | 3 = 19.3 in.

55. $-2x^2 - 9x + 14$ **56.** $-4y^2 + 4y + 3$

57. $-12m^3n^7$ **58.** $10x^4 - 35x$ **59.** $-27r^6t^9$

60. $x^2 + 12x + 27$ **61.** $x^2 - 3x - 28$

62.

x	−2	−1	0	1	2
f(x)	−7	2	5	2	−7

Post-Course Test

1.

Students that Graduated

Number of students vs. Year of graduation (1995, 1996, 1997, 1998, 1999, 2000)

Post-Course Test *continued*

2. 690 students **3.** Each year, between 4 and 6 more students graduated than the previous year. Because 235 students graduated in 2000, there were probably about 240 students that graduated in 2001. **4.** 21 **5.** 25 **6.** 5 **7.** 7 **8.** 28 m; 49 m^2 **9.** 44 yd; 120 yd^2 **10.** 17; -17 **11.** 24; 24 **12.** -43 **13.** -32 **14.** $-$ **15.** -120 **16.** 132

17. -6 **18.** $6 + x$ **19.** $9a - b + 7$ **20.** 6 **21.** $\frac{3}{5}$ **22.** -4 **23.** -3.3 **24.** -42.5 **25.** 5 **26.** 5 **27.** -10 **28.** 12

29. $x \geq -8$;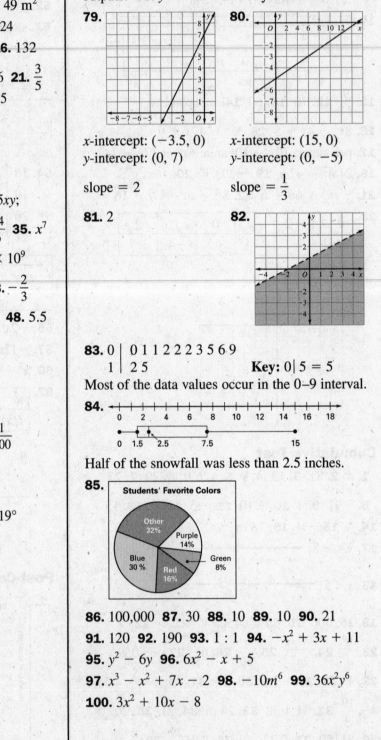
-9 -8 -7 -6 -5 -4 -3 -2 -1

30. $x > -3$;
-5 -4 -3 -2 -1 0 1 2 3

31. GCF = 8; LCM = 224 **32.** GCF = $5xy$; LCM = $35x^2y^2$ **33.** $\frac{42}{8} > \frac{20}{4}$ **34.** $7\frac{1}{3} = \frac{44}{6}$ **35.** x^7 **36.** $\frac{1}{x^5}$ **37.** y^5 **38.** 0.0000721 **39.** 3.68×10^9

40. 131; 130; 130; 94 **41.** $1\frac{1}{2}$ **42.** $2\frac{1}{2}$ **43.** $-\frac{2}{3}$ **44.** $\frac{5}{8}$ **45.** -4.86 **46.** 2.911 **47.** -29.28 **48.** 5.5

49. -2 **50.** 2 **51.** 63 **52.** 54

53. $y > 8$;
6 7 8 9 10 11 12 13 14

54. $n \leq 2$;
-5 -4 -3 -2 -1 0 1 2 3

55. 16 cm **56.** 0.345; $\frac{69}{200}$ **57.** 0.0025; $\frac{1}{400}$

58. $9.53 **59.** $11.25 **60.** $\frac{4}{19}$

61. 39°

62. $m\angle 2 = 119°$, $m\angle 3 = 61°$, $m\angle 4 = 119°$

63. 2160°

64.

$\triangle ABC$ is similar to $\triangle A'B'C'$.

65. 2, 7, -12 **66.** $\sqrt{0.5}$, 0.7, $0.\overline{77}$, $\frac{15}{18}$, $\frac{8}{9}$

67. 10 m **68.** $x = 6$ in.; $y = 6\sqrt{2}$ in.

69. $\sin = \frac{25}{65}$, $\cos = \frac{12}{13}$, $\tan = \frac{5}{12}$ **70.** 113.04 ft^2

71. 87.5 in.^{2} **72.** 5 faces, 8 edges, 5 vertices **73.** 753.6 cm^2; 1306.24 cm^3 **74.** 1500 mm^2; 3600 mm^3 **75.** No; -8 has two outputs. **76.** $y = -x + 2$ **77.** yes **78.** no

79.

80.

x-intercept: $(-3.5, 0)$ x-intercept: $(15, 0)$
y-intercept: $(0, 7)$ y-intercept: $(0, -5)$

slope = 2   slope = $\frac{1}{3}$

81. 2

82.

83.

0	0 1 1 2 2 2 3 5 6 9
1	2 5

Key: $0 \mid 5 = 5$

Most of the data values occur in the 0–9 interval.

84.
0 2 4 6 8 10 12 14 16 18
0 1.5 2.5 7.5 15

Half of the snowfall was less than 2.5 inches.

85.

Students' Favorite Colors
Other 32%
Purple 14%
Blue 30%
Green 8%
Red 16%

86. 100,000 **87.** 30 **88.** 10 **89.** 10 **90.** 21 **91.** 120 **92.** 190 **93.** 1 : 1 **94.** $-x^2 + 3x + 11$ **95.** $y^2 - 6y$ **96.** $6x^2 - x + 5$ **97.** $x^3 - x^2 + 7x - 2$ **98.** $-10m^6$ **99.** $36x^2y^6$ **100.** $3x^2 + 10x - 8$

101. $f(x) = 3x - 1$

Input, x	$f(x) = 3x - 1$	Output, $f(x)$
-2	$3(-2) - 1$	-7
-1	$3(-1) - 1$	-4
0	$3(0) - 1$	-1
1	$3(1) - 1$	2
2	$3(2) - 1$	5

102. yes **103.** no

Algebra Readiness Test

1. 11.4 **2.** 80 **3.** 6.4 **4.** 14.76 **5.** 2.048

6. -11.2 **7.** 16.2 **8.** 10 **9.** 200 **10.** $x - 105$

11. $x + 4$ **12.** $\dfrac{16}{x}$ **13.** $x = 1.2(16)$ **14.** $15x = 45$

15. $2(16 + x) = 20$ **16.** $3\left(\dfrac{x}{2}\right) = 6$

17. $\dfrac{x}{6} = x - 4$ **18.** -96 **19.** -517 **20.** 84

21. -601 **22.** $y - 69$ **23.** $4a + 7b$ **24.** 10

25. $5r - s$ **26.** $-\dfrac{f}{2}$ **27.** $\dfrac{2b}{3}$ **28.** $-\dfrac{1}{3}$ **29.** $-\dfrac{7}{8}$

30. $-\dfrac{3}{20}$ **31.** $1\dfrac{7}{18}$ **32.** -6 **33.** $-1\dfrac{1}{15}$ **34.** -4

35. 13 **36.** 15 **37.** 10.5 **38.** -4 **39.** -12

40. 168 **41.** -9.9 **42.** -1 **43.** 7 **44.** 6 **45.** 1

46. $-\dfrac{1}{3}$ **47.** $-\dfrac{1}{3}$ **48.** $\dfrac{15}{28}$ **49.** $-\dfrac{2}{3}$ **50.** 6 **51.** 4

52. 2.5 **53.** -4.6 **54.** 18 **55.** -3.7 **56.** 41.4

57. 6.084 **58.** 6 **59.** $\dfrac{1}{2}$ **60.** -4 **61.** 9 **62.** 5

63. -2 **64.** 2 **65.** 7 **66.** ± 6 **67.** ± 40 **68.** ± 11

69. ± 3 **70.** ± 6.56 **71.** ± 1.02 **72.** 15 **73.** 8

74. A number is less than or equal to -2.

75. Nine is less than a number. **76.** Twice the sum of a number and 1 is greater than 6.

77. The quotient of a number and -12 is greater than or equal to 3.

78. $x > 2$ **79.** $x \geq \dfrac{7}{3}$ **80.** $x < -80$ **81.** $x > 22$

82. $g > 3$ **83.** $t \leq \dfrac{1}{2}$ **84.** $2 \cdot 2 \cdot 2 \cdot 2 \cdot a \cdot b$

85. $5 \cdot 11 \cdot x \cdot x \cdot x \cdot y \cdot y \cdot y \cdot y$

86. $2 \cdot 3 \cdot 3 \cdot 7 \cdot f \cdot g \cdot g \cdot g \cdot h$

87. $3z^4$; $45z^7$ **88.** $14w$; $42w^2x$ **89.** $20ab$; $200ab^3c^5$

90. m^3p; $1482m^8np^2$ **91.** $\dfrac{-4y}{13x}$ **92.** a^{11}

93. g^8 **94.** $4d^{13}e^2$ **95.** 5 **96.** 28 **97.** 4 **98.** 43.8

99. 6 **100.** 8 **101.** $t = -\dfrac{r}{2}$ **102.** $t = 3 - r$

103. $f(x) = -4x^2 + 16$ **104.** yes **105.** no **106.** yes

107. no **108.** no **109.** no **110.** no **111.** no

112. $y = -\dfrac{1}{3}x + 3$ **113.** $y = x - 5$

114. $y = -2x + 7$ **115.** $y = 44$

116. $y = -\dfrac{1}{2}x + 3$ **117.** $y = -x + 3$

118. $-x^2 + 10$ **119.** $y^2 + 2y + 3$

120. $5x^2 - x - 2$ **121.** $-x^2 + 8x - 4$

122. $-12n^6$ **123.** r^6t^4 **124.** $x^2 + 13x + 36$

125. $4x^2 + 11x - 3$

Answers

Diagnostic Pre-Course Test Performance Record

Skills Review Handbook Topic	Test Exercises	Date _____ Test Performance
Number Sense		
Place Value, 759	Exs. 1, 2, 3, 4	_____/4
Rounding, 760	Exs. 5, 6, 7, 8, 9, 10, 11, 12	_____/8
Divisibility Tests, 761	Exs. 13, 14, 15, 16	_____/4
Mixed Numbers and Improper Fractions, 762	Exs. 17, 18, 19, 20, 21, 22, 23, 24	_____/8
Ratio and Rate, 763	Exs. 25, 26, 27, 28	_____/4
Number Operations		
Adding and Subtracting Decimals, 764	Exs. 29, 30, 31, 32	_____/4
Adding and Subtracting Fractions, 765	Exs. 33, 34, 35, 36	_____/4
Solving Problems Using Addition and Subtraction, 767	Exs. 37, 38	_____/2
Multiplying Fractions, 768	Exs. 39, 40, 41, 42	_____/4
Multiplication of a Decimal by a Whole Number, 769	Exs. 43, 44, 45, 46	_____/4
Dividing Decimals, 770	Exs. 47, 48, 49, 50	_____/4
Solving Problems Using Multiplication and Division, 772	Exs. 51, 52, 53	_____/3
Measurement and Geometry		
Points, Lines, and Planes, 773	Exs. 54, 55, 56, 57	_____/4
Angles, 774	Exs. 58, 59, 60	_____/3
Using a Ruler, 775	Exs. 61, 62, 63, 64, 65, 66, 67, 68, 69, 70	_____/10
Using a Protractor, 776	Exs. 71, 72, 73, 74	_____/4
Using a Compass, 777	Exs. 75, 76, 77, 78	_____/4
Data Analysis		
Reading and Making Line Plots, 782	Exs. 79, 80, 81, 82, 83	_____/5
Reading and Making Bar Graphs, 783	Exs. 84, 85, 86, 87	_____/4

McDougal Littell Math, Course 3   **S1**
Assessment Book

COURSE 3 Continued
Diagnostic Pre-Course Test Performance Record

Skills Review Handbook Topic	Test Exercises	Date _____ Test Performance
Reading and Making Line Graphs, 784	Exs. 88, 89, 90	_____/3
Venn Diagrams and Logical Reasoning, 785	Ex. 91	_____/1

Remediation Notes: _____

_____

_____

_____

COURSE 3
Diagnostic Pre-Course Test
Item Analysis

Exercise Number	Skills Review Handbook Topic	Date _____ Class Tally of Responses
	Number and Number Sense	
1	Place Value, 759	
2	Place Value, 759	
3	Place Value, 759	
4	Place Value, 759	
5	Rounding, 760	
6	Rounding, 760	
7	Rounding, 760	
8	Rounding, 760	
9	Rounding, 760	
10	Rounding, 760	
11	Rounding, 760	
12	Rounding, 760	
13	Divisibility Tests, 761	
14	Divisibility Tests, 761	
15	Divisibility Tests, 761	
16	Divisibility Tests, 761	
17	Mixed Numbers and Improper Fractions, 762	
18	Mixed Numbers and Improper Fractions, 762	
19	Mixed Numbers and Improper Fractions, 762	
20	Mixed Numbers and Improper Fractions, 762	
21	Mixed Numbers and Improper Fractions, 762	
22	Mixed Numbers and Improper Fractions, 762	
23	Mixed Numbers and Improper Fractions, 762	
24	Mixed Numbers and Improper Fractions, 762	
25	Ratio and Rate, 763	
26	Ratio and Rate, 763	

Diagnostic Pre-Course Test
Item Analysis

Exercise Number	Skills Review Handbook Topic	Date _____ Class Tally of Responses
27	Ratio and Rate, 763	
28	Ratio and Rate, 763	
	Number Operations	
29	Adding and Subtracting Decimals, 764	
30	Adding and Subtracting Decimals, 764	
31	Adding and Subtracting Decimals, 764	
32	Adding and Subtracting Decimals, 764	
33	Adding and Subtracting Fractions, 765	
34	Adding and Subtracting Fractions, 765	
35	Adding and Subtracting Fractions, 765	
36	Adding and Subtracting Fractions, 765	
37	Solving Problems Using Addition and Subtraction, 767	
38	Solving Problems Using Addition and Subtraction, 767	
39	Multiplying Fractions, 768	
40	Multiplying Fractions, 768	
41	Multiplying Fractions, 768	
42	Multiplying Fractions, 768	
43	Multiplication of a Decimal by a Whole Number, 769	
44	Multiplication of a Decimal by a Whole Number, 769	
45	Multiplication of a Decimal by a Whole Number, 769	
46	Multiplication of a Decimal by a Whole Number, 769	
47	Dividing Decimals, 770	
48	Dividing Decimals, 770	
49	Dividing Decimals, 770	

McDougal Littell Math, Course 3
Assessment Book

Diagnostic Pre-Course Test
Item Analysis

Exercise Number	Skills Review Handbook Topic	Date _____ Class Tally of Responses
50	Dividing Decimals, 770	
51	Solving Problems Using Multiplication and Division, 772	
52	Solving Problems Using Multiplication and Division, 772	
53	Solving Problems Using Multiplication and Division, 772	
	Measurement and Geometry	
54	Points, Lines, and Planes, 773	
55	Points, Lines, and Planes, 773	
56	Points, Lines, and Planes, 773	
57	Points, Lines, and Planes, 773	
58	Angles, 774	
59	Angles, 774	
60	Angles, 774	
61	Using a Ruler, 775	
62	Using a Ruler, 775	
63	Using a Ruler, 775	
64	Using a Ruler, 775	
65	Using a Ruler, 775	
66	Using a Ruler, 775	
67	Using a Ruler, 775	
68	Using a Ruler, 775	
69	Using a Ruler, 775	
70	Using a Ruler, 775	
71	Using a Protractor, 776	
72	Using a Protractor, 776	
73	Using a Protractor, 776	

Diagnostic Pre-Course Test
Item Analysis

Exercise Number	Skills Review Handbook Topic	Date _____ Class Tally of Responses
74	Using a Protractor, 776	
75	Using a Compass, 777	
76	Using a Compass, 777	
77	Using a Compass, 777	
78	Using a Compass, 777	
	Data Analysis	
79	Reading and Making Line Plots, 782	
80	Reading and Making Line Plots, 782	
81	Reading and Making Line Plots, 782	
82	Reading and Making Line Plots, 782	
83	Reading and Making Line Plots, 782	
84	Reading and Making Bar Graphs, 783	
85	Reading and Making Bar Graphs, 783	
86	Reading and Making Bar Graphs, 783	
87	Reading and Making Bar Graphs, 783	
88	Reading and Making Line Graphs, 784	
89	Reading and Making Line Graphs, 784	
90	Reading and Making Line Graphs, 784	
91	Venn Diagrams and Logical Reasoning, 785	

McDougal Littell Math, Course 3
Assessment Book

COURSE 3 Post-Course Test Performance Record

Lesson Title	Test Exercises	Date _____ Test Performance
Chapter 1: Variables and Equations		
Interpreting Graphs, 1.1	Exs. 1, 2, 3	_____ /3
Order of Operations, 1.2	Ex. 4	_____ /1
Variables and Expressions, 1.3	Exs. 6, 7	_____ /2
Powers and Exponents, 1.4	Ex. 5	_____ /1
Variables in Familiar Formulas, 1.6	Exs. 8, 9	_____ /2
Chapter 2: Integer Operations		
Integers and Absolute Value, 2.1	Exs. 10, 11	_____ /2
Adding Integers, 2.2	Exs. 12, 13	_____ /2
Subtracting Integers, 2.3	Ex. 14	_____ /1
Multiplying Integers, 2.4	Exs. 15, 16	_____ /2
Dividing Integers, 2.5	Ex. 17	_____ /1
Number Properties, 2.6	Ex. 18	_____ /1
The Distributive Property, 2.7	Ex. 19	_____ /1
Chapter 3: Solving Equations and Inequalities		
Solving Equations Using Addition or Subtraction, 3.1	Exs. 20, 21	_____ /2
Solving Equations Using Multiplication or Division, 3.2	Exs. 22, 23, 24	_____ /3
Solving Two-Step Equations, 3.3	Exs. 25, 26, 27, 28	_____ /4
Solving Inequalities Using Multiplication or Division, 3.7	Exs. 29, 30	_____ /2
Chapter 4: Factors, Fractions, and Exponents		
Greatest Common Factor, 4.2	Exs. 31, 32	_____ /2
Least Common Multiple, 4.4	Exs. 31, 32	_____ /2
Comparing Fractions and Mixed Numbers, 4.5	Exs. 33, 34	_____ /2
Rules of Exponents, 4.6	Exs. 35, 36, 37	_____ /3

Student _____ Teacher _____ Course _____

Post-Course Test Performance Record

Lesson Title	Test Exercises	Date _____ Test Performance
Scientific Notation, 4.8	Exs. 38, 39	_____/2
Chapter 5: Rational Number Operations		
Fractions with Common Denominators, 5.1	Ex. 41	_____/1
Fractions with Different Denominators, 5.2	Ex. 42	_____/1
Multiplying Fractions, 5.3	Ex. 43	_____/1
Dividing Fractions, 5.4	Ex. 44	_____/1
Adding and Subtracting Decimals, 5.6	Exs. 45, 46	_____/2
Multiplying and Dividing Decimals, 5.7	Exs. 47, 48	_____/2
Mean, Median, and Mode, 5.8	Ex. 40	_____/1
Chapter 6: Multi-Step Equations and Inequalities		
Solving Equations with Variables on Both Sides, 6.2	Exs. 49, 50	_____/2
Solving Equations Involving Circumference, 6.4	Ex. 55	_____/1
Solving Multi-Step Inequalities, 6.5	Exs. 53, 54	_____/2
Chapter 7: Ratio, Proportion, and Percent		
Writing and Solving Proportions, 7.2	Exs. 51, 52	_____/2
Fractions, Decimals, and Percents, 7.4	Exs. 56, 57	_____/2
Percent Applications, 7.6	Exs. 58, 59	_____/2
Simple Probability, 7.8	Ex. 60	_____/1
Chapter 8: Polygons and Transformations		
Angle Pairs, 8.1	Ex. 62	_____/1
Angles and Triangles, 8.2	Ex. 61	_____/1
Polygons and Angles, 8.4	Ex. 63	_____/1
Similarity and Dilations, 8.8	Ex. 64	_____/1

McDougal Littell Math, Course 3
Assessment Book

Student _____ Teacher _____ Course _____

Post-Course Test
Performance Record

Lesson Title	Test Exercises	Date _____ Test Performance
Chapter 9: Real Numbers and Right Triangles		
Square Roots, 9.1	Ex. 65	_____/1
Rational and Irrational Numbers, 9.2	Ex. 66	_____/1
The Pythagorean Theorem, 9.3	Ex. 67	_____/1
Special Right Triangles, 9.5	Ex. 68	_____/1
Using Trigonometric Ratios, 9.6	Ex. 69	_____/1
Chapter 10: Measurement, Area, and Volume		
Areas of Parallelograms and Trapezoids, 10.1	Ex. 71	_____/1
Areas of Circles, 10.2	Ex. 70	_____/1
Three-Dimensional Figures, 10.3	Ex. 72	_____/1
Surface Areas of Prisms and Cylinders, 10.4	Ex. 73	_____/1
Surface Areas of Pyramids and Cones, 10.5	Ex. 74	_____/1
Volumes of Prisms and Cylinders, 10.6	Ex. 73	_____/1
Volumes of Pyramids and Cones, 10.7	Ex. 74	_____/1
Chapter 11: Linear Equations and Graphs		
Relations and Functions, 11.1	Exs. 75, 76	_____/2
Equations in Two Variables, 11.3	Exs. 77, 78	_____/2
Graphs of Linear Equations, 11.4	Exs. 79, 80	_____/2
Using Intercepts, 11.5	Exs. 79, 80	_____/2
Slope, 11.6	Exs. 79, 80, 81	_____/3
Graphs of Linear Inequalities, 11.8	Ex. 82	_____/1
Chapter 12: Data Analysis and Probability		
Stem-and-Leaf Plots, 12.1	Ex. 83	_____/1
Box-and-Whisker Plots, 12.2	Ex. 84	_____/1

Teacher Name _____ Class Period _____

Post-Course Test
Performance Record

Lesson Title	Test Exercises	Date _____ Test Performance
Using Data Displays, 12.3	Ex. 85	_____/1
Counting Methods, 12.4	Ex. 86	_____/1
Permutations, 12.5	Exs. 87, 88, 91	_____/3
Combinations, 12.6	Exs. 89, 90, 92	_____/3
Probability and Odds, 12.7	Ex. 93	_____/1
Chapter 13: Polynomials and Functions		
Polynomials, 13.1	Exs. 94, 95	_____/2
Adding and Subtracting Polynomials, 13.2	Exs. 96, 97	_____/2
Monomials and Powers, 13.3	Exs. 98, 99	_____/2
Multiplying Binomials, 13.4	Ex. 100	_____/1
Non-Linear Functions, 13.5	Exs. 101, 102, 103	_____/3

Remediation Notes: _____

_____

_____

_____

COURSE
3

Post-Course Test
Item Analysis

Exercise Number	Lesson Number	Date _____ Class Tally of Responses
1	1.1	
2	1.1	
3	1.1	
4	1.2	
5	1.4	
6	1.3	
7	1.3	
8	1.6	
9	1.6	
10	2.1	
11	2.1	
12	2.2	
13	2.2	
14	2.3	
15	2.4	
16	2.4	
17	2.5	
18	2.6	
19	2.7	
20	3.1	
21	3.1	
22	3.2	
23	3.2	
24	3.2	
25	3.3	
26	3.3	
27	3.3	
28	3.3	
29	3.7	
30	3.7	
31	4.2, 4.4	
32	4.2, 4.4	
33	4.5	
34	4.5	
35	4.6	
36	4.6	
37	4.6	
38	4.8	

Teacher Name _____   Class Period _____

Post-Course Test
Item Analysis

Exercise Number	Lesson Number	Date _____ Class Tally of Responses
39	4.8	
40	5.8	
41	5.1	
42	5.2	
43	5.3	
44	5.4	
45	5.6	
46	5.6	
47	5.7	
48	5.7	
49	6.2	
50	6.2	
51	7.2	
52	7.2	
53	6.5	
54	6.5	
55	6.4	
56	7.4	
57	7.4	
58	7.6	
59	7.6	
60	7.8	
61	8.2	
62	8.1	
63	8.4	
64	8.8	
65	9.1	
66	9.2	
67	9.3	
68	9.5	
69	9.6	
70	10.2	
71	10.1	
72	10.3	
73	10.4, 10.6	
74	10.5, 10.7	
75	11.1	
76	11.1	

Post-Course Test
Item Analysis

Exercise Number	Lesson Number	Date _____ Class Tally of Responses
77	11.3	
78	11.3	
79	11.4, 11.5, 11.6	
80	11.4, 11.5, 11.6	
81	11.6	
82	11.8	
83	12.1	
84	12.2	
85	12.3	
86	12.4	
87	12.5	
88	12.5	
89	12.6	
90	12.6	
91	12.5	
92	12.6	
93	12.7	
94	13.1	
95	13.1	
96	13.2	
97	13.2	
98	13.3	
99	13.3	
100	13.4	
101	13.5	
102	13.5	
103	13.5	

Student _____ Teacher _____ Course _____

Gridding Sheet

McDougal Littell Math, Course 3
Assessment Book